PERRY BURGESS

WHO WALK ALONE

Presented to —
Mrs. Vanderbilt Webb.
with the compliments of the
author —
Perry Burgess

New York

HENRY HOLT AND COMPANY

To Cora, my wife

WHO IS MY COMPANION ON MY VISITS
TO THOSE ILL WITH HANSEN'S DISEASE
(LEPROSY) AND WHO THOUGHT THIS
STORY SHOULD BE TOLD

ILLUSTRATIONS

An aerial view of Culion   frontispiece

Rice terraces in northern Luzon   16

San Lazaro dormitory   88

Balala, and the colony proper   104

Houses of the patients—and the inner bay   105

The little bay in Coron   128

One of the hospitals at Culion—and Tomas at a clinic   140

The back country of Culion   140

A typical street in the colony—and the leper cemetery   141

Tomas with his fighting cock, Mystery   152

Fishermen's houses and one of their native fish traps   178

General Wood at Culion   200

New Leonard Wood Memorial Laboratory   264

The Leonard Wood Monument—and the square in
   front of Colony Hall   265

AN EXPLANATION

This is the story of an American soldier who served in the Spanish-American War in the Philippines, and who many years after he had returned home became a leper. He is not the only American soldier who experienced that fate. More than thirty became patients at the great leper colonies at Culion or at Cebu, in the Philippines, or at the United States Leprosarium in Louisiana.

I have told Ned's story because I knew him well, because he has now joined his comrades who have answered the last muster, and because his heroic and successful efforts to cope with this new and frightening world in which he suddenly found himself impressed me as one of the great human sagas. I have known personally many of these American veterans, as well as scores of others who, despite this apparently hopeless handicap, have faced their new world with as much courage as did Ned. For many the separation from their old life has meant losses as great, or greater, than his. Some had already established their families and left behind them wives and children—some were further advanced on a successful career than was he.

In offering this book as a tribute to Ned, I am tendering it to all those others who have fought or are fighting silently and alone one of the most tragic battles that can confront men anywhere. The incidents credited to Ned are in all essentials those which he experienced. I have added from the actual experiences of others whom I have known only enough additional material to obscure his identity and preserve the self-imposed anonymity under which some of the people whom the book touches are living at this very moment. For understandable reasons, I have used fictitious names wherever the use of true ones might affect the lives and careers of the actual persons. However, these prototypes have not been fictionalized or distorted to make a more sensational book. In every germane respect, this is both a true and a genuine narrative.

The story had to be written in this personal fashion since no man I ever knew was more real, more actually alive than Ned Langford—his dogs—his house—his business—his wish to die under the flag he had served—his bags of wild game. I was with him once when he and Brant returned from the cogon with three wild hogs. His delight was that of huntsmen everywhere. As Ned said of his father, so it could be said of Ned: "He was a man."

"It is strange that men should see sublime inspiration in the ruins of an old church and see none in the ruins of a man."—CHESTERTON.

WHO WALK ALONE

CHAPTER ׳ ׳ ׳ ׳ ׳ ׳ ׳ ׳ ׳ ׳ ׳ ׳ ONE

J UST WHEN OR WHERE THE THING THAT WAS to bring my life to an end had happened I never knew. It was impossible to know. It was certainly sometime between the day I landed with a regiment of Colorado volunteers at Cavite and the day I sailed for home at the end of the Philippine Insurrection. That it had happened I did not even know for nine more years. . . .

In the spring of 1898 I was in my third year of college. On this particular day I was sitting in my room trying to get something out of a textbook in chemistry, and listening for the lunch bell. Suddenly it rang and I got up yawning. The football coach had had us out for spring practice at an ungodly hour that morning. Even so, it seemed to me the bell was premature. Then a siren started somewhere and church bells began to peal.

I hit the stairs four at a time to see what was up. Bob Sellars, my roommate, grabbed me as I reached the bottom step. Bob was the varsity fullback; I played end.

3

"We're on our way, Ned!" he shouted. "War has been declared against Spain!"

We ran out on the campus; students were coming from all directions. The band had gathered and we fell in behind. It seemed to me the whole five hundred of us were there; not counting most of the faculty.

Until this time the band had just been tooting and booming, but as we got into formation Dexter, the bandmaster, shouted something that was lost to everyone but the band members. Up went his arms, and with a smash that seemed to shake the air they swung into "There'll Be a Hot Time in the Old Town Tonight!"

We all went quite mad. We marched through the streets of the town, with the townspeople lining up along the sidewalks and cheering. After two hours of this all of us were half dead—except seventy-year-old Prexy who led the procession. Head up, chin out, he was better than any of us. Maybe our little old college band wasn't great shucks but it certainly was on the warpath that day.

Spain was going to pay for it—sink our ships—run poor little Cuba ragged—she was at long last going to pay for it and we students were going to help see that she did.

We didn't have long to wait. Uncle Sam asked for seventy-five thousand volunteers. They started a regiment in Colorado and many of us enlisted. Soon we were in camp and they were trying to make soldiers of us. We could shoot, but that was about all any of us knew of soldiering.

There was a lot of talk and a good deal of excitement about an outfit that was being trained at San Antonio. They were mostly cowboys and Indian fighters—Roosevelt's

Rough Riders, they were called. Teddy Roosevelt was a colorful fellow from New York who came out here quite often to ride wild bronchos and shoot grizzlies. Their colonel was a man named Leonard Wood. We had heard of him— he was an army medico who had covered himself with glory fighting Indians, and particularly Geronimo. I decided, if I could wangle it, I was going to get transferred to that crowd. Bob Sellars had the same idea. We learned that Colonel Wood was to stop off and inspect our troops on his way to San Antonio and we made up our minds to get to him someway with a request to take us along. We didn't get very far with that. I did finally manage to get a word with one of the aides and was told they already had far more men than they could take and we would have to stay put.

I had just finished talking with the aide and had turned around to go back to my tent when I ran smack into Wood. What a man he was—tall, straight, bronzed and lean, with something about him that seemed to mark him as a leader. I stood aside quickly, and saluted. He returned the salute gravely and ran me over with his eagle eye. He smiled. It warmed me up all over. Then he had gone, but that smile never quite went with him. "As one soldier to another," it seemed to say; it gripped me. I would have given anything to go with him.

We had been in camp several weeks when rumors began to spread that we were probably going to the Philippines. That excited us tremendously, our imaginations having already been fired by Dewey's victory over the Spanish fleet in Manila Bay. Then they gave us three days' leave and we took that to mean we should soon be moving out.

Three days didn't leave me much time at home but I made the most of them. My people lived in Missouri at the foothills of the Ozarks. The rambling old house had been home for us Langfords for three generations. Our nearest city of any size was Zarika, about ten miles away.

When I arrived at the station you'd have thought I was a visiting prince. The depot was full. There was dad, with his chest out, and with him mother. Back of them, Tom and Mabel. And they had all come down to the depot in the carriage, although the house was a scant mile away! Old Wash stood at the horses' heads with the air of owning most of the earth and the usual loungers had increased by a half hundred. I wanted to duck, but dad stepped forward and grabbed my arm, and mother just put both arms around me then and there. I got creepy inside. Tom and Mabel were so shy you might have thought I was a stranger instead of the big brother they plagued until he licked the daylights out of them.

I had a couple of days at home. The next thing I knew I was on board the *China*, General Greene's flagship and by all odds the best of our fleet. There were over a thousand of us on the ship: First Regiment, Colorado Volunteers— which meant us—half a battalion of U. S. Infantry, and a small detachment of U. S. Engineers.

We were sailing. The *China* and the *Senator* were slipping out into the bay, heading west. I felt the throb of the engines like a pulse in the deck beneath my feet.

"Here you go, landlubber! Many a day before you set foot on good, old, solid earth again!" The blast from the whistle seemed to shake the whole ship and then all the boats in the harbor joined in. The fleet with four thousand fighting men was on its way to Manila. The *Colon* and the *Zealandia* dropped in behind us, and we steamed toward the Golden Gate.

After the first hour or so I was too busy to notice the other ships. There was a cocky little corporal with the regulars who seemed bent on making this war miserable for me. We didn't actually mix it up until the glorious Fourth. On that day they gave us leave from the usual routine. Boy, was that a mistake! There were several private feuds just ready to hatch. Bob and I were leaning over the aft rail in comparative obscurity. We were both feeling a little homesick and I guess we looked it.

"Missing mamma, little boy?"

I looked up and saw friend corporal standing with both hands on his hips grinning at me. I was in no mood to take more from that smart Alec and let fly at his chin, which I barely grazed, he jerked his head so fast. He slammed a hefty one to my left jaw—I could count the stars one by one! It was a peach of a fight. Some of those babies really came tough in the regulars. It was lucky for me that I was in good training. We went at it nip and tuck until Bob yelled,

"Down him, kid!" I made a flying tackle, taking him hard around the waist. We went down with a crash, knocking his breath out. His buddy who had been standing by started toward us, but Bob laid a hand on his arm.

"Calm yourself. This isn't any of your business."

"Get off me! What in hell you tryin' to do, play football? That's no kind of fightin' for a soldier." I rolled off and we got to our feet. He was grinning. He stuck out a big paw.

"O.K., little boy. You'll do. No hard feelings." We shook.

We were steaming steadily south, and I was learning what a tropical night could be. The full moon was riding high in deep blue and casting so bright a carpet of silver that the stars would fade out in its brilliance. There was a spot in the shadow of a lifeboat. I haunted it whenever I could get there. I'd lie there and think of home, of mother and dad, of a girl—well, she wasn't really much my girl only you had to think of some girl on such a night.

Corregidor looked like a great emerald at the mouth of Manila Bay. We crowded the deck to stare as we came nearer.

"Say," said Bob, "the bay's a beaut, isn't it?" And it was. Fifteen miles across the entrance I could hardly see the highlands at the other side. We swung around to the east and made toward Manila, almost thirty miles away. On our portside rose the highlands of Luzon. We stood wondering if the war was still on. When we were close in a dispatch boat came out. We learned that the war was still on, all right.

They landed us at Cavite. On the smooth waters of the harbor floated the blackened hulls of such of the Spanish vessels as had not been actually sunk in the fighting. We got our first sample of tropical rain, as we made camp that night. It poured. We waded in mud. Our pup tents and blankets were soaked, but it was so hot we fairly steamed. Our cooks fussed around swearing as they tried to start fires.

In the morning the rain had stopped and we began to enjoy the tropical sunshine. In a few days we were moved toward Manila. The Spanish army was cooped up within the walls of the city. "Intramuros," they called it, which meant, literally, "within the walls."

There was very little serious fighting. It seemed such a pity that any of our men or the Spaniards should have had to lose their lives since there was no possible chance for the Dons to escape. They were shut off on the rear by the Filipinos and by the American army and fleet on the sea side.

When the city finally fell we all thought we would soon be on our way home. In a way that was disappointing, for we had seen nothing of the Philippines except the part between the sea and the Pasig River which runs through the city of Manila. To our surprise we stayed on and on. Rumors began to spread that there was likely to be trouble with the Filipinos. We understood that they were demanding immediate independence, which the American leaders were unwilling to grant.

During this time Bob and I were getting a tremendous kick out of Intramuros. That walled city had three hundred years of history behind it. Cannon thrust through deep embrasures and sentry posts for the guards, were brand new in our lives. Grand old buildings, hundreds of years old! The ancient palace; there was a new palace out on the Pasig River, called Malacañan, but the old palace still stood. The beautiful cathedral, even the government buildings, not much like American state houses. We were in a story-book world. Long sloping approaches led up to the high parapets, and from that vantage point you could look far out across Manila Bay where Dewey's fleet rode at anchor, and across the Pasig River where the Filipinos were entrenched. Back of that lay the real Philippines.

On moonlight nights Bob and I, when it could be managed, would climb to the top of the walls. Mystery and glamour lay over the barrios across the river. We wondered and longed to know what was there. Those of the Filipinos whom we had met we liked very much. They were kindly, courteous, obliging and gentle. When we were moving up to Manila I had been billeted for a day or so with an old cochero who drove a little Spanish pony hitched to a carromata, a Philippine edition of an American victoria, only higher and on two wheels. Juan worked from early morning until late night, his faithful beast going on an all-day trot—he was never permitted to walk—his tiny hooves clattering in unison with thousands of other ponies, the chanted music of Manila.

Juan's home was typical of the poor Filipino. It was made of nipa palms and bamboo. It stood on posts several feet above the ground and was entered by a ladder. It consisted of three small rooms, a tiny kitchen, a storage room, and a general living and bed room. The few centavos he earned were sufficient to supply his family with simple vegetables and rice and, on rare occasions, a little fish, and a scant portion of grain for the pony. I shall never forget how kindly they received me—a stranger forced upon them —and how Rosario strove to give me of their very best. They were enormously happy at my interest in their shy, brown children, a half dozen of them. That was my first acquaintance with a Filipino family and the years that followed only deepened the impression of a friendly, kind, likeable people.

The situation with respect to the Philippine army became more serious as the summer dragged on and the fall came. Few of us soldiers knew anything about the justice of the differences which had arisen. The Medical Corps boys worked overtime and kept us busy filling in the old moat that surrounded the walled city, and cleaning up generally. Smallpox and typhoid were rife and there were whispers of Asiatic cholera. Months passed and there was no indication that we were likely to be sent home. Finally the order went out that the Filipino soldiers were not to be permitted to enter our lines bearing arms.

It started shortly after that order was given. About midnight on the fourth of February a lone soldier, one of the Nebraska volunteers, who was stationed at a bridge, saw three Filipino soldiers crossing to our side. He challenged; they would not stop and he fired. One of the men fell. At once both sides were ablaze. Along the whole line the Krags of the Americans and the Mausers of the Insurrectos were barking out the pent-up resentment of the past months. This was war—real war. By morning the Americans were across the river and well into the country beyond. One California regiment was in such a hurry that in its ignorance of the country it became completely lost. We kidded those boys about that until the end of the war.

Reorganization of the army began. Many of us whose terms of enlistment had expired, volunteered for regular units. I soon found myself a permanent adjunct to Uncle

Sam's army, embarked on the wild goose chase of trying to catch the subsequently famous Emilio Aguinaldo.

Our first severe fighting was just outside Manila. The Insurrectos had been expecting us; we found them well entrenched. There were some twenty regiments of us, I understood, and we had to cover about an eighteen-mile line. Our advance was steady but it was tough going. We were in the trenches for forty-three days and it rained about twenty hours out of every twenty-four. We wallowed and slipped and fell in mud, and we looked like hogs.

On the tenth, the day we took Caloocan, I had a bit of adventure. My captain sent me off with a message to a unit of Montana volunteers. I cut across country, keeping under cover as best I could. I came through a patch of bamboos out into the clear. Across the rice paddies I saw a big, stone building. That, I thought, would be the headquarters of the command. So far as I could see there was not a soul in sight, friend or enemy. I looked about cautiously and started to cross on a trot. Someone was about all right! I heard the whine of a Mauser and dirt flew up into my face. Then they began biting all about me. I put on steam—I was through the gate when I heard men yelling,

"Where do you think you're going, you damned fool?"

"That's a home for lepers!"

I jumped back from that gate as though I'd been hit. My heart missed a beat. A home for lepers? It must be a joke. I had heard about lepers in Sunday School but I didn't dream they still existed. The voices had come from behind the stone walls of a cemetery across the road. The Montana boys must be there. I crossed in nothing flat, and found myself in the midst of a company of American soldiers. They were using the cemetery wall as breastworks and firing fitfully toward a wood some distance away. I delivered my message to the captain, and was ordered to remain there under cover. As the firing increased I could see the inmates of the house across the way going hell bent for leather through the fields. Lepers, it seemed, had no more relish for hot lead than anyone else. I couldn't understand it. Why wouldn't they welcome death? I was certain that if I were a leper, a bullet would seem a good out.

The next months were crammed full of experiences which I never forgot. The battle of San Jacinto was fought and won, only to find that Aguinaldo had slipped away again. Our work was cut out for us. The Insurrectos knew the terrain and fought hard and gallantly. We pressed on, fighting much of the way. Always the Wily One just escaped us. We heard that he was in Bontoc, the capital of the head-hunting country, so we set out for Bontoc. We were just in time to see the rear guard of the Insurrectos disappearing up the trail to Mount Polis, a peak towering over the ranges at a height of a mile and a half. Worn out, we camped in the plaza of the town. The people flocked about us curiously: naked children, women wearing only sarongs; men, G-strings. Some of the women looked beautiful until you got a glimpse of their lips, which were blood-red from the incessant chewing of the betel nut.

One night of resting and we were once more on Aguinaldo's trail. That fellow was as smart as they come. We followed him up over Mount Polis to Banaue, an experience to be remembered to the end of a man's days. We

were passing through the region of the rice terraces, certainly one of the wonders of the world. For three thousand
years the natives have edged up the sides of the mountains
with their handmade terraces. Up the slopes they have
toiled with loads of stones balanced in crude baskets suspended from a pole across their shoulders. The stones they
have carefully laid as facings. Sometimes these walls rise
thirty, forty and even fifty feet. With unremitting toil they
have carried earth to enrich these rice fields. They have
diverted mountain streams for irrigation. Rice farms green
with growing grain edged at right angles into the mountain
sides from the valley to the very top. There were hundreds
of separate levels, each with its contribution toward sus-
taining life. Out of these barren mountains a wild and
ignorant people have improvised granaries sufficient to fill
every hungry mouth.

Aguinaldo gave us the slip again. We never did catch up
with him. That was left for Funston. But we were in
Aguinaldo's debt for having led us through some of the
most beautiful country on earth. We were returned to
Manila, and soon after, he was captured and the insurrection collapsed, although guerilla fighting went on. I was
moved about some, spent a little time in the southern
islands. Then I was returned to Luzon.

My memory holds fast to a humdrum session of garrison
duty in a little town in the south. We were a small detachment and we were billeted in the homes of the Filipinos.
I stayed with a family by the name of Nolasco. They were
of the upper class, with a home far more comfortable than
the average. They lived in a wooden house, with wood

floors instead of the usual bamboo. With characteristic hospitality, they gave me a room of my own, a luxury with all the charm of novelty. And there was a daughter, as beautiful as any Filipino I had seen—and some of the girls were as fair and fragile and lovely as Dresden. Carita! Her very name "little face" seemed to me exquisite. I thought I was in love and had some sessions with myself about marrying and settling down in the Islands.

Then my term of enlistment was up and suddenly I was impatient to be home, to see mother and dad, the family and the old friends about town.

T
HEY MET ME AT THE STATION AGAIN.
By the time I could reach the train steps and swing down,
the family was there. Old Wash and the horses were missing and the family was getting out of a brand-new, horseless
carriage. I hadn't seen half a dozen of them altogether, because machines were scarce when I went to the Philippines.
I was almost as much interested in it as I was in the folks,
and the people milling around. The crowd began to cheer
and a town band, of sorts, began playing "Hands Across
the Sea."

It made me feel like a fool until a kid took it out of me
by whispering loud enough for anyone to hear, "Gee, he
ain't even got a uniform."

Evidently the town had been expecting more than it was
getting.

Mother looked just the same, smiling and saying little.
But there were tears in her eyes as she put her arms about

(top) *Rice terraces in the Mountain Province, northern Luzon, Philippines.*

(bottom) *The view which greeted Ned Langford on the chase after Aguinaldo from Bontoc, capital of the Mountain Province, to Benaue.*

me. Dad slapped me on the back and took both my hands in his.

"It's great to have you back, boy."

I didn't like the way dad looked. He had aged a lot and there was a deep pallor in his face. Mabel had changed most. It didn't seem possible that the very attractive young lady, in what appeared to my inexperienced eye, an outlandish costume, long ruffled sleeves, tight waist, flaring skirt, with more ruffles sweeping the ground and an enormous hat with a pair of bird's wings—very stylish she told me later—could be the gangling kid I had left four years before. Tom was just plain boy. He must be nearly thirteen, tall and husky. He grinned as he stuck out a fist as big as a man's.

"Did you get shot anywhere?" he demanded at once. Then he wanted to know how many "Philistines" I had killed, and whether I had got any gold. The papers had been printing a lot about the resources of the Islands. Dad finally managed to shut him off and introduced me to the mayor and a few others in the crowd that pressed about us.

I had begun my part in the Spanish-American War with a parade, and was about to finish with another. The collapsible canvas top was folded back over the high rear seat of the automobile. The band formed in front of us, and a hundred or so of the townsfolk who had come to welcome me fell in behind. Tom cranked the engine. When it started it sounded like a Gatling gun. We went up Main Street at a snail's pace with the storekeepers and customers coming out onto the sidewalks to wave at us. We stopped at the town park just across from the fire house. There was a band stand I had not seen before. With no explanation

I was invited to get out and to mount the platform. The folks, beaming, came along, and we sat in front of the band while the mayor and a local minister I did not know made flattering speeches, and I felt I wanted to go through the floor. Then they called on me.

I was a great disappointment. All those nice people were just yearning to hear bloodcurdling tales of fighting. They wanted to know all about the terrible head-hunters and the dog eaters they had read of in the newspapers. And all I could think of were the little towns of Luzon with their peaceful plazas and old stone churches, their nipa houses and rice paddies with the water buffalo wallowing through them, pulling a crooked stick for a plow. I thought of the people, of the old cochero with whom I had been billeted, of Maximino Nolasco and my lovely Carita whom I had nearly married. What I had to say was in high praise of the Filipinos and although the audience was polite enough, I'm afraid my speech fell flat.

At last they let us go. But for months I was stopped on the street and asked question after question. Tom was just a pest. He kept at it day and night and really wormed the most of it out of me bit by bit. He even got on to how I felt about Carita.

"Whyn't you marry her?" he asked, grinning. "You like her well enough, even now. She sounds good to me."

She was good. I knew that. I wondered when I should hear from her. We had taught each other something of our own languages, she drilling me in Tagalog and I trying to instruct her in English. We had agreed that she was to write to me in English and I would reply in Tagalog. But the months passed and no letter came.

The family seemed to take it for granted that I needed a vacation. So for some time I loafed about, going over the farms and lounging around the business. Dad had two farms, the North and South farms we called them. At Zarika, he conducted a business of trucking and warehousing. It had grown while I was away; dad had added several branches in neighboring cities. He was running about a hundred trucks and vans and a good-sized warehouse for storage. He hauled anything—merchandise, mining machinery or furniture—and the business was flourishing.

One morning I went down to the office with dad. We got there early, just as the horses—there were more than two hundred in the stables—were coming down the long ramps leading from the second floor to the ground, where the vans and drays were waiting for them. Those perfectly matched teams with their shining harness made a beautiful sight. I hung around while he went over the mail, and as I waited I stared out the window looking toward the warehouse platforms where freight cars were unloading.

"Ned," said dad, "I wanted to get you alone. What are you figuring on doing?"

"I don't know. I don't feel that I can go back to college and finish there. I'm too old, and the war has made a difference—"

"How would you feel about joining me? It's a good business. I ought to know, I built it myself."

He watched me keenly. He was offering me his kingdom! I had no notion how good I would be at running such a business, and said so. Also I had a kind of uprooted feeling. It was hard to bring my mind to settling down. But I said nothing of that; you couldn't say that to a father who was offering his kingdom. I thanked him for making the offer and asked for time to think it over.

"Sure, Ned. Want you to. Don't rush into it. Take your time."

At the end of the week I told him I would join him, and if I made good would stick with it.

Dad braced right up after that and began breaking me in with a vengeance. I knew, or rather guessed, that this was because he was really a very sick man. He refused to see a doctor; he had never had a doctor in his life. His obstinate stand distressed mother and she asked me to urge him to get medical care. I tried, but dad told me curtly that he knew what ailed him and that he was prepared to take care of himself. Before that winter passed he was an invalid. We had a doctor at the last and dad laughed and offered to diagnose for him. Horace Windle was a young practitioner and had gone to school with me. He told me that my father was exactly right and that nothing could be done but to make it a bit easier for him. During the following summer, he died. All in all, what with the business he had built and his sticking it out to the end, I figured that my dad was a man.

I went on with the business, and Tom, who loved it, spent much of his time out of school there. I had been home seven or eight months and I had written to Carita twice but had received no reply. Then one day I got a letter from Bob Sellars, who had stayed on out there and enlisted in the constabulary. He had just returned from southern Luzon where he had seen the Nolasco family. Carita had asked him to write me why I had never heard from her:

her younger brother, Sancho, had been discovered to be a leper. He had been sent to the home I had seen that day I carried the message to the unit of Montana boys. But Carita feared others of the family might be infected, and she had been too worried to write.

I was stunned. Leprosy. The very word chilled my blood. Poor Maximino, poor little Carita. It was some time before it struck me that I had lived in that house. I had slept on their floor, I had eaten of their food. I had a moment of wild terror. Then finally I could think about it sensibly. It was eight months since I had come back and I was sound and whole. My fear for myself passed and I fell to thinking about Sancho. He was just a kid. I supposed that leprosy was carried like a sex disease, through sleeping with someone who had it. But Sancho was not old enough for that. How could he have caught it? I gave it up. But I kept thinking of Carita and her danger. She must have sensed it too, or she would have written. The thought of that lovely "little face" being exposed to anything so horrible seemed unbearable. I got out my horse and rode far into the country, returning long after nightfall. When Tom tried to kid me about Carita, I told him what had happened to Sancho. He listened gravely and said he was very sorry. He was a fine boy. He never mentioned the Nolascos again, and his attitude toward me altered subtly. I think he knew I was suffering.

Life settled down to a busy day-by-day existence. We had plenty to do, running two farms and a business. I say "we" because Tom was a real help. He finished high school and went away to college. But there were the long vacations when he pitched in like a man. Indeed Tom at eighteen was a man, and we were all proud of him.

I had been back nine years when in a single instant life stopped being humdrum and became electric. Of course it was a girl. She came with her brother to a party and the minute I laid eyes on her I could see nothing else. She was the prettiest thing I had ever seen and she had a voice colored with laughter. I've never known a girl who was so gloriously happy. My courtship of Jane was like our racing after Aguinaldo over Mount Polis and the northern ranges of Luzon—tempestuous and swift. Only we never got Aguinaldo, and within a month Jane had agreed to marry me.

"But not yet," she said. "I owe it to father and mother to finish school."

Jane was attending a school in the East, specializing in music. She was an accomplished pianist and did some composing. Her people had recently taken over a large farm near us and she felt they had sacrificed to send her to this school and that she must graduate. One night she played something new for me, the most haunting melody I had ever listened to.

"What is it?" I demanded. "I've never heard it before."

Jane laughed. "Of course you haven't, darling, since I just wrote it—for you." I made her play it over and over. When I learned it I went around whistling it all day.

That haunting air became a bond between us. I had met Jane on her Easter vacation. She returned to school, but came back that summer, the happiest of my life.

One night early in September Jane and I had driven in to

Zarika to a concert and we had stopped at the office on the way home. Jane was sitting by the window humming our song when we heard the fire alarm. We leaped to our feet and I threw open the door to the main office. The night watchman was running toward us.

"The third floor of the warehouse is afire. The stables may catch."

There were three men on duty in the stables at night, Old Wash and two others. Wash was coming down the right ramp as we entered.

"Sumthin' afiah, Mistuh Lanfud. Looks lak hull town afiah out de back winders."

"You two boys stay on the ramps," I yelled as the other two raced down. "Wash and I will cut them loose. Hit them as they come down. Keep them going."

"Dey's cumin' right down."

Wash and I headed for the horses, but Jane caught up with us and pleaded with me not to go. It did look pretty bad. The place was beginning to light up outside, but the stable was still clear. I pushed Jane back but she held on, crying that she was going too. At that moment Tom materialized. He was going up.

"Here, Tom!" I yelled. "I'll see to the horses—you take care of Jane." As I got to the floor above I could see Tom with Jane hanging over his shoulder like a sack of bran. She was fighting and kicking.

"Take them from the back stalls first, Wash! Wash, where are you?"

"Yas, suh. I is adoin' it!" I heard the smack of Wash's big black paw on his first horse and a dappled gray clattered into the lane and headed for the ramp. I grabbed a feed shovel and joined him. We heard yells from below; help had arrived. We heard the crash of the warehouse roof as two more men came up.

They were yelling from below for us to come out. I had a little saddle mare and as luck would have it she was at the farther end. The roof was ablaze when I got to her and she, being high-strung, was the dickens to handle. A spark blew into her manger and the hay leaped into flame. I tried to turn her and she pulled me against the side of the manger and knocked the breath out of me. My arm went into the flaming hay and a stab of pain shot to my shoulder. I slapped her across the face and she backed out. Old Wash sprang to the other side as we got her into the lane between stalls. All the others were out. We got her down as the place behind us became a sea of fire.

Jane was almost hysterical, Tom still holding her. She saw my burned sleeve and then my arm. She was greatly distressed, and insisted on winding a handkerchief about it.

"Does it hurt much, Ned?"

"My hand hurts like sin."

"But your arm! You're badly burned on the forearm, on the back."

I twisted my arm around. It was burned and burned badly. But I didn't seem to feel it.

Horace Windle drove up just then. Jane called him and he had his kit open in a jiffy and was beginning on my arm.

"Fix the hand, Doc," I said. "It hurts like the devil."

"Your arm must hurt like two devils then."

"But it doesn't," I shouted. "Fix the hand. I guess I know what hurts."

He fixed them both. We stood around a bit and then he

said, "See here, Ned, come up to my office as soon as you can and I'll do a better job. Those burns are rather severe."

"Go along," Tom said. "I'll get the men and round up the horses."

Jane and I drove up to Windle's. He made a thorough job of it this time, going over my entire arm. Even with the burns he found a numb area on the forearm.

"Say, Ned, sure you didn't get nipped by a bullet or nicked by a bolo in that spot? Or maybe an army mule kicked you?"

"Of course not, you nut. What's so queer?"

"Nothing, as far as I can see. Only people usually don't go numb in spots without some reason. Anyhow it's saved you pain from the burns so it's all to the good and you should worry."

Jane and I went back and picked up Tom.

"The fire is out, Ned, and we've found all the horses."

"Jane," I said, "if I had faded out tonight, this youngster of a brother of mine could run the whole shebang."

"Aw," muttered Tom, "don't you go believin' him, Jane."

CHAPTER THREE

Hectic and busy months followed the fire. With settling insurance, letting contracts for fireproof buildings, buying new vans and trucks, my days were overfull. Among our purchases were two of the new motor trucks. We were proud of our horses, but this type of automobile was, without doubt, the transportation agent of the near future. When we bought our first two there were only about six thousand in the entire country. Believe me, we had plenty of trouble, as breakdowns were frequent. Tom had completed his college course and wanted to go off right away to one of the automobile manufacturing plants to learn something about them at first hand. We all liked the idea, as the whole family was more or less batty about motors. After three months Tom returned with some knowledge and unbounded enthusiasm. He started in by persuading me to buy one more, giving us three altogether. He got me sufficiently interested to spend a lot of time with him studying their innards; what made them go and kept them going.

The future was beginning to look rosy. Jane had gone back to complete her last year at school, and we planned to be married in June. Both mother and Mabel were very fond of her, and as Mabel had a love affair of her own, she and Jane had been very thick and the two kept up a constant correspondence. Before Jane left we had actually begun work on our house. It was located near the river and the woods on the South place. Watching the building take shape meant daily visits of inspection. I hardly had time to be lonesome. Overseeing all the construction meant running back and forth from farm to town.

My burns had healed up in reasonable time. But those curious, numb spots remained. Horace Windle was convinced they came from some injury I had forgotten.

At Christmas I had Jane back with me. Those were glorious days and nights. I played hooky from business, leaving it to Tom. Cold as it was, Jane and I spent our time mooning about our partly built home during the day, and we were at some party or other practically every night. It was tough, seeing her go off again, but I consoled myself with the thought that it was the last time, and that there were only five months more of waiting. As her train pulled out, she stood on the rear platform and waved to me until she faded to a speck in the distance.

Back at the office I found a letter from Bob Sellars. Bob had become more or less a fixture in the Philippines. He was a major in the constabulary. During recent years he had spent a lot of time down in the southern islands, particularly Mindanao, in scraps with the Moros. They were vicious fighters, those Moros. As Mohammedans they believed that if they wanted to make sure of paradise their best bet was to go out and bolo a heathen to death. "Heathen" to them meant the despised Christians, whether Filipino or Americano. I got a laugh out of that. What a world! We called them heathen; they thumbed their noses and said "the same to you" and started for you with a bolo.

This letter told me nothing of my old friends. But before a month had passed I got another. Sancho, Carita's brother, had been sent to an island called Culion. The Americans had established a leper colony down there. Culion was about two hundred miles south of Manila on the edge of the China Sea. Bob said they had good doctors in charge there, and they held high hopes of developing a cure for this strange disease. His letter contained surprising news of Carita. She had married some time before and had gone to Cebu. Shortly afterwards her husband had died. There had been a baby who had not lived. I wrote at once to Bob asking if there was anything I could do. I wrote to Maximino and Carita, too, saying nothing of Bob's news, just telling them something of my affairs and that I thought of them often.

Spring was almost here. In a few months Jane would be boarding the train for home, our home. I was humming away in the shower when I thought of that spot on my forearm. I had forgotten it. I twisted up my arm.

A queer feeling ran through me, beginning, it seemed, at my heart and seeping like icy water down through my veins. There was a second spot, high up on my shoulder! I put up an experimental finger and pressed my nail into the center.

Strange. It was like the first, without feeling. I stepped out of the shower, went to my dressing case, took out my nail file and pressed its point into the center of the whitish area. There could be no doubt: there was no feeling there.

Dressing as quickly as possible, I told mother not to wait breakfast for me, I would eat in town. I took the car and drove straight to Windle's house. Katherine came to the door. As a doctor's wife she was not surprised at early morning calls. She showed me into the office and called Horace.

As soon as he came in, I burst out, "See here, I've got another of those damned spots."

He went over both spots again, looking at them through a glass. Finally he went into his laboratory and came back with a long needle. "This may hurt a bit, we'll just see." I shut my eyes to make a fair test.

"Feel that?"

"No. What do you think it is?"

"I don't know, Ned. But it's foolish to get so nervous. The fact that I don't know doesn't mean a thing. Skin troubles are many and elusive. You need a man who specializes in them. I want you to see Dickson, you know him."

He was a new man in town. I knew him but slightly.

"I'll phone him if you like, Ned."

Struggling into my shirt, I answered,

"Well, I've hardly had a sick day in my life, Horace. All those years in the Philippines, the fellows had all sorts of things. But I escaped. And we lived, well—you'd hardly believe me if I told you how we did have to live sometimes. I don't want anything the matter with me. All right, you phone Dickson; if he can see me I'll go right over."

A half hour later Dickson had finished looking me over. It was evident the thing had him stumped.

"There is no point in my telling you that I know what this is. Frankly I don't know. It is a condition which I never have seen. If I were in your place I would go to one of the large cities and let some man who has had more experience than I have had, see it."

Well, that was that. I'd had precious little need for doctors in my whole life, and then when I did need them, they had to tell me that they couldn't do anything for me! I went home, took another shower, scrubbed my arm until it was nearly raw, poured a lot of straight alcohol over it, got into some fresh linen and went back to the office.

There was a lot to do those days, but not much got done while the thought of the spots kept gnawing at me. The scars from the fire I did not mind. I had earned them. But these two ugly things, which came from nowhere, and wouldn't go away—that was something else.

It must have been about a month after my visit to Dickson that the thing really hit me. Maybe it had been lurking in my subconscious mind all that time and I hadn't dared let it out into the open. What Dickson said stayed with me; I had thought that I might try to get to some big city, St. Louis or Kansas City possibly, before Jane returned. One night I was going through some old letters. I had burned most of those from Bob, particularly those about Sancho and Carita, for I had talked about those friends of mine and except for Tom, I didn't want anyone to know of their misfortune. Among some of Jane's letters I came across one from Bob which in some way had missed the fire. I sat there with it in my hand. This time I faced it squarely;

those weeks in the Nolasco house—Sancho—Carita—those
spots on my arm.

Everybody was in bed and the house was dark. I felt my
way down the stairs and wandered off across the fields. The
whole thing was ridiculous. For nine years I had been
home. I was whole and strong. The doctors thought nothing of those spots. Horace Windle thought they were from
an old injury, no—he had thought that about the first one.
Accidents? I had been hurt in a football game, yes, but that
was the other shoulder. Once my horse had stepped into a
hole and had thrown me. That memory was hazy; I
couldn't recollect whether I had been hurt or where. The
coming of dawn made me realize that I had wandered all
night. I was down where our home was being built. For a
time I stood looking at it, then turned and walked briskly
back to the house. I did not look at the spots. But it was
no use. Look at them or not, I could not keep my mind
off them.

The contractor came to the office to see me about some
changes I was making in the type of fire doors in the new
warehouse. When he went I sat slumped at my desk, pon-
dering. Where could a fellow find out about any kind of
disease? I hated asking around until every doctor in town
knew that there was something wrong with me. The library
had medical books, but a man couldn't walk into his home
library and say to a librarian who'd known him since he was
a pup, "Please give me all the books on disease, particularly
skin diseases!"

Tom came in to tell me about one of the horses that was
sick. His new love of motors had not affected his first love,

horses, in the least. I'd rather have had him and old Wash doctoring a horse any time than our regular vet.

"Cold this morning?"

"No, why?" And then I realized that I was not working in rolled-up shirt sleeves as was my habit.

"Oh, that, just forgot to take my coat off. Henderson came in early to talk over those doors." Tom went out whistling my song, my song and Jane's. The son of a gun liked to tease me that way, knowing it made me jealous.

On the way home that night it occurred to me that I might get some information from the Bible. As soon as I was alone in my room after supper I started hunting. After a couple of hours I had found nothing that seemed suspicious. Then I thought of "Ben Hur." There was something in that book about it. Must be a copy around the place somewhere, probably in the attic. Armed with a candle I went up. After poking around in boxes and closets I located the novel in an old trunk full of books, carried it down to my room and found the place. Ben Hur had searched for his mother and sister and when he found them they had run away from him, calling to him not to come near and crying, "Unclean! Unclean!" I read the description and laid the book down with a great sigh of relief. I looked nothing like that. It was insane to be so upset. Satisfied, I got into bed and slept, making up for the night before.

"Say, what's up? Got good news from Jane?" Tom and I were on our way to town the following morning.

"No news, why?"

"Well, you've been going around all morning like the

wide-eyed little lark. I believe it's orthodox to whistle in your bath. But when it comes to humming between mouthfuls of eggs and bacon, well! From the way mother looked at you she must think you have gone batty. Dear brother of mine, I am sure you have no idea what a relief it will be to your family, when you two love birds have finished your nest."

Grinning at him, I let it go at that.

A week later I was exercising my privilege of whistling in my bath, bestowed by that swell kid brother of mine, when I happened to look down. A third spot, like the others! This one was on my leg. I was both frightened and angry, angry that the thing should progress like this when there was no reason for it, angry that it should continue to force itself into my life just when I wanted to be left alone with my happiness, frightened because no one knew what these spots were. I had to know!

In Dickson's office he studied the third spot.

"You told me long ago that I should see someone who might know, Doctor. Tell me where to go. I am ready, today."

"The best man I know is in St. Louis. When I was in medical school I had a lot of work with him. He teaches part time at Washington University. I'll wire and tell him to expect you."

Back at my office I telephoned mother and asked her to send some clothes down. I was going out of town for a few days on business, and hadn't time to get home. The truth was, I was afraid to let her kiss me good-by. Luckily, Tom was out. I left a note about some insurance rates we were trying to get lowered, and said that I had to go out of town to straighten out a mix-up on material for our house.

At one o'clock I was peering out of the window of the Pullman, wondering when, and under what circumstances I should return.

Though I did not dare to put it into words, what I now feared colored every one of my acts. To avoid all other people I took a drawing room. When dark fell outside the windows I lay down on the couch in all my clothes. No sleep was possible. In the early morning the train arrived at St. Louis. I walked and walked. Mastering my courage, I finally got to the point of heading for the doctor's office. Nothing must be said to arouse his suspicions, and yet with this fear on my mind I was likely to blurt out anything.

At last I went into the building and found his offices on the third floor. It was an elaborate establishment, a reception room with half a dozen men and women waiting, and other doors down a corridor, one of them bearing the name of Watkins, the man I had come to see. Twisting my hat in my hands, I stood in the middle of the floor until a nurse appeared.

As soon as I mentioned my name she said the doctor had been expecting me and would see me as soon as he could. She asked me to sit down but I couldn't be still. I went to a window and looked out over the city without seeing it. Should I have written to Jane? We wrote every day; I ought to write her today. And mother, she must have been hurt at my leaving so abruptly. I'd write her, too. That insurance, Tom would manage that all right. . . . Just then the nurse came back and called me.

She led me down the corridor into a room, mentioned my name and vanished. I was facing a man of perhaps fifty-five, gray but youngish looking, with an air of assurance and success about him. At once my doubts left me. This man would fix me up.

"Dr. Dickson sent me a wire about you, Mr. Langford. Good man, Dickson. It's a pity to bring you all this way, just to see me. Well, let's have a look. I was reading about your firm and the fire some months ago. Nice piece of work getting all those horses out. I like horses."

I had stripped to the waist and he was looking at the spots.

"These all?"

"One on my leg," I admitted and took off my trousers. He prodded the spots and went over me carefully. He asked about my health and my family. There was no intention on my part to speak of my service in the Philippines, but he got to that, and kept right on, questioning, questioning. Then he told me to dress.

"Look here," he said. "This is the queerest thing I have ever seen. There are some things that might account for these spots, but apparently they do not apply to you. I am afraid I don't know what I can do for you. And, worst of all, I don't know what to tell you to do."

I stared. Here was a big man, puzzled. More than that, he was an honest man, and I could see how worried he was by his own inadequacy. I was on the rack and needed help. He knew it. He would do anything he could. It was plain that if he was to help me, I must help him.

"Doctor," I began; my voice was strained and queer. "Doctor—could it be leprosy?"

He looked at me in amazement. It seemed a full minute before he spoke. Those honest, clear eyes looked straight into mine. "Why do you ask that?"

It all came out then, about Sancho and Carita; the four years in the Islands, moving as ordered from one place to another, sleeping in the houses of the natives; or, after many hours of marching, in the plaza of some little town. I told him of the nights when we lay huddled together, soldiers and passengers, on the deck of some little inter-island boat, of weeks in monasteries and old Spanish forts, of the Lepers' Home I had nearly blundered into.

"If it hadn't been for Bob Sellars' letters," I finished miserably, "I might never have connected it all up. But I keep thinking it might be—and no one knows a thing—and I'm going to be married in June."

The way he looked at me showed that he understood the hell I had been living through the past months. "My boy,"—no one had called me "boy" for years—"I never saw but one case of leprosy in my life. When I was an interne in medical school we had one case. At least that is what it was finally called. I remember reading up on the disease at that time. But frankly, I don't know whether this is leprosy or not. I don't know whether there is anyone in the city who would know." He walked to the window and stared out for a few minutes. Then he turned back to me.

"See here. Suppose you give me some time. Go out and forget it for a while. Come back in a couple of hours. Don't worry. If I find anyone worth while, I'll arrange for you to see him at once."

I left that office knowing no more than when I went in. But I had found a friend. And at last I had found courage to speak of this thing. What a relief to get out into the open after months of guarding my tongue! For the next two hours I walked the streets or sat in a park near the doctor's office, thinking about all the strange circumstances that brought me to the city on such an errand. About doctors: how terrible it must be to know that people come to you for help and that you don't know what to do for them. Here was a man who probably had a wife and family and a life of his own. Yet he had taken me on, as if I belonged to him.

When I went back there was no waiting; the nurse took me in at once. Dr. Watkins was excited and pleased.

"I've found just the fellow for you," he said, smiling. "Major Thompson. He was in the Medical Corps of the army for years, and some of the time he spent in the Philippines. He has retired from the army now, but practices in the city. I don't know him personally, but I've made sufficient inquiry to be certain that he is a good man. I hope that he will be able to clear this thing up for you. He is expecting you, there will be just time for you to make the appointment, if you take a taxi."

It was useless to try to thank him or pay him. He said I

had nothing to thank him for, and he would take no pay. He shook hands—I was always grateful for that. Despite what he knew, he took the chance and shook hands.

Major Thompson was the type of man I would have recognized anywhere. Hard-boiled, matter of fact, tough. He was the sort who had made the troops safe in the malarial and cholera districts of the Islands. Ruthless, he followed his conviction, a life or two meant nothing, it was the conquest of the disease that counted.

"Watkins told me about your service," he began. "What outfit were you with?"

"Colorado Volunteers to begin with. I stayed on through the Insurrection with the regular army. Spent a lot of time in the Mountain Province."

"Then I'll bet you were in the bunch that couldn't catch Aguinaldo? That old boy was too smart for you."

I was hot all over.

"Listen, Major. Dr. Watkins sent me here to find out what's wrong with me. I don't give a damn about Aguinaldo. I want to know what the hell these spots mean."

"I'm sorry. But you are the first Carabao who has blown in here since I set up practice. Come along, let's look at you and see whether Uncle Sam is responsible."

He touched my spots with a pin while I kept my eyes closed.

"Billeted in Philippine homes?"

I went over it again, Maximino and Sancho and Carita.

"Huh!—You liked this girl, eh?"

"Yes, Major. I thought for a time of marrying her and settling down in the Islands."

"Uh, huh. Had a girl like that myself in Cervantes, in Ilocos Sur, nice little thing too. Ever up there? No? Now I'd like a little sample of you, just a snip off one of those spots."

"Take as many as you like. I want to know what's the matter with me and I'm tired of being passed about and nobody knowing."

He snipped a piece of each spot. It didn't hurt. He ran a swab up each nostril and smeared a slide.

"Have to ask you to wait a bit. . . . Like to have a look at these."

I watched him intently as he poured some sort of dye on the slides, and held them up, for a few moments, to dry. Then he washed them off under the tap, blotted them and carried them over to a narrow table, where he sat down before a microscope. He slipped one of the pieces of glass into place, and moved a screw on the side back and forth.

I was fascinated. The noise of the city outside faded away. The room in which we sat contracted. There were just the two of us: the major bending over a microscope and I sitting—watching—waiting. He drew out the first slide and inserted another. . . .

I thought of a story I had read years ago of a man standing unblindfolded before a firing squad.

Suddenly he pushed his chair back and leaped to his feet.

"There's no doubt about it, none at all. It's the old Hansen bacillus, sure's you live."

Wheels started going round in the top of my head. Hatred flamed in me. I wanted to kill him! Happy as a king, all over a bug! And I had the bug! If I had carried a gun, I think I would have shot him. I turned to the door, staggered and caught at the frame. At once he was beside me.

"Oh, God, soldier, I'm sorry. Come and sit down. I've a little Napoleon brandy; let me pour you a bit. Let's have a drink to the old days. I'm not letting you down. Honest to God I'm not. Let's have a good stout snifter and then we'll talk it all over."

But it wasn't that which moved me. It was that knowing, he put an arm about me and guided me to a seat. I gulped my brandy and pushed back my glass for more—and more.

"Doc," I mumbled, "is it hopeless? Is there no cure at all?"

"Well, there *is* a new treatment and there's a lot of hope that it's going to work." He went on and on, and something of his spirit passed over into me. I began to sit straighter and to breathe easier.

"You've been thinking for a long time," he said, "but now you have to think some more. I'm going to fix things so we can be together quite a lot in the next few days. Eventually I will have to report your case to the Department of Health. I know you must have a few days to get hold of yourself. I happen to know of a deserted shack down the river a ways. What say I take you down there this afternoon? I'll get you things to eat and see you settled. And I can run down every day until things can be worked out."

I told him I'd do anything he suggested.

We drove along by the river. Soon the city was behind us; there were just a few houses here, unpainted farmhouses or log cabins. We turned from the highway down a rutted lane toward the river. The car stopped. I got down, still dazed, and stood. I never moved while Thompson took some things to a kind of unpainted shack which had a picket fence running around it. He kept on talking. After a time he said, "I'll have to be going now. I'm sorry I can't stay with you. I'll be out early tomorrow." And with that he drove away.

I stood looking after him, how long I do not know. It might have been an hour later when I turned and gazed across the wide Mississippi. There were trees, not quite green, far across on the other bank, or maybe on an island. I walked down to the river edge and watched the drift. Time again passed, still I stood there staring. Then I started to walk upstream. Birds, startled, flew up from their nests in the bushes. Sometimes a fish leaped out of the water—it was spring!

Around a slight bend I came upon it. As far as I could see along the bank and inland stretched an unbroken desert of debris, millions of cans, old crates, old iron, decaying fruit and vegetables, the neighborhood's dump. The stench was terrible. I stood there looking. What a lot of stuff! The wreck of what had been a baby carriage was at my feet—a baby carriage! There was an upturned wooden box. I sat on it. Again time went by. At last it came to me. Here by this dump I belonged. Refuse, that was Ned Langford.

I mulled it over and over. It was happening. But still it was behind a curtain, unreal. And I was away off watching it. I did not look at the dump again; I knew I belonged to it. The sun was going down; it had gone down. But the moon had come up and it guided me to the shore. I wanted to watch the river. It licked in to the edge of the bank and with every lap a bit of soil went. Mud, mud! That was the way mud was made. Mud, going down to the Gulf where it built up land again. A fallen log jutted into the water. I sat down. There were things coming along all the time, bits of wood, cans, pieces of cloth. And time went on, and on. The current out in the middle was swift. If a man were to swim out there and just drift he could go down, down to the Gulf with the drift and the mud. Just let go. I fixed my eyes upstream on a small, round thing that came nearer and nearer. I couldn't make it out. Then the current swept it toward the bank and for a time it floated at my feet, turning, turning. A shudder ran through me. I stepped back. I hated rats, and this one was dead. Death wiped out everything. Maybe this rat was poisoned. Maybe the river caught it in a whirlpool and drowned it. Maybe it was just old. Maybe someone caught it in a trap and then it was dumped with the garbage. Maybe, maybe—on and on—and on. The wind was rising and an eddy carried the filthy thing away.

Long after it had gone, long after the moon had crossed and dropped behind the trees, I sat on the bank. The river belonged to the rat; he had got there first. The river was his, not mine. I must have walked again for I was back by the garbage dump, sitting on a box. I felt something racing over my ankle. It was a rat. A live rat! Not the rat floating in the river, but a hungry, live rat from the dump. There were more of them. I leaped to my feet, shouting and kicking. Squealing, they raced away and I could hear them scuttling to their havens in the piles of refuse. There was a faint light from the east by which I groped my way and found the shanty. The door stood open. As I came up there was a sound of slithering feet. A horde of brown rats scurried out and made past me for the dump. I kicked against the sides of the shack to frighten the last few and went in, closing and bolting the door. In the dim light I peered about. There was one left, a huge devil of a rodent in the far corner, disputing possession with me. I started to the door to unfasten it, when, without warning, he flew at me, hit my leg with terrific force, his teeth ripping through my trousers. I lurched back, but I caught him with my foot and kicked, sending him against the opposite wall. He squealed shrilly and flew at me a second time. I snatched up the only chair and hurled it, and the thing went to pieces. He had turned and was on me again. This time he leaped high and I struck at him with my clenched fist as he clung to my coat. He dropped to the floor. I kicked at him but missed; he was too quick for me. I stopped to pick up the chair leg and like lightning he was on my hand, tearing, tearing! I grabbed frantically and found his throat. He let out one bloodcurdling squeal as my hands closed on him. He fought and clawed, cutting my hands until the blood streamed. I was afraid to let go. He was limp, he must be dead, but I hung on. Then I swung my arms and hurled him, dead, through the glass in the window.

With the sound of breaking glass something crashed within me. Alone, alone for all time: Mother! Mabel! Tom! Jane! Jane . . . Jane . . . for the first time in my memory I began to sob. I reeled across to the wooden bunk, threw myself down, and wept my heart out.

CHAPTER ✦ ✦ ✦ ✦ ✦ ✦ ✦ ✦ ✦ ✦ ✦ FIVE

Someone was pounding. it was broad daylight. Half awake, I opened the door; it was the army medico. He stared at my torn clothing and bloody hands. Then he came in and looked around.

"What the devil happened?"

"Rats. One tackled me."

He pointed to my lacerated hands. "Bite you?"

"And scratched me. The place is alive with them."

"Oh, yes—the dump. Better fix your hands right away. My bag is in my car." He went out and returned with his kit.

"Where's the water?" I indicated the milk can in which we had brought water from the city the day before. He found pans and poured some water into them.

"I'll have to boil this. Man, look at the bread!" He held up the remnant of a loaf the rats had left and threw it out of the door. He ripped paper wrappings from the groceries, and stuffed the paper into the stove, picked up pieces of the chair, broke them over his knee and thrust them on top of the paper. In a moment he had a roaring fire. When the water boiled he treated my hands.

"Did he nip you any other place?"

"Don't think so. You see I killed him with my hands. He did hit my leg once."

"I'd better see it." There was one small scratch, which he disinfected.

"Have you had anything to eat?"

"No. I didn't come in until almost morning. The rats were here. This one got fastened in when I locked the door."

"Those devils are vicious when they're cornered. When did you eat last?"

"I—I really can't remember."

"Before you came to me, yesterday?"

"I had some coffee. I couldn't eat."

"Huh, good thing I brought more food. Not much left here." He was still clearing up, throwing things into the stove and chattering. I made a move to help, but he brushed me aside.

"I'm a temperamental cook and I can't be bothered. Stay put, will you?" He washed off the top of a rickety old table, and covered it with a newspaper which he must have brought out the day before. In one of the boxes were plates, and two cups.

"Tomorrow I'll bring out some more groceries." He was down on his knees with his head halfway inside a small cupboard.

"Holy mackerel! Look at this!" He pulled out a rusty old skillet full of spiders' webs, and started in to scour it.

"Well, apparently they don't like coffee; it's all here. And I brought some eggs, bacon and rolls. Good thing I did; they pretty well cleaned you out. Did I tell you I was with the Utah Light Artillery? One of our first fights was at Caloocan—the Insurrection wasn't a week old then. And boy, that fight was a pippin!"

Caloocan—I heard again the whine of the Mausers and voices shouting.

"Where do you think you're going, you damned fool?— That's a home for lepers."

He saw me wince but he rambled on, telling of more fights, of miserable tramping through tropical rains, of Filipino beauties; he seemed to have had an eye for the girls. Then breakfast was ready.

"Come and get it, soldier. Get it quick or our friends will be back with us. Haven't had breakfast myself so I'm joining you."

We ate it all.

"What about the dishes?" I asked finally. "Should I throw them out, or what?"

He said nothing for a moment, and then remarked gently, "Don't worry so much. You can boil everything."

A funny thing happened. I couldn't remember his name!

"I'm ashamed to tell you. I don't know your name."

"No wonder! Man, you've had a shock! It's Bill. Thompson's the other half."

Then I remembered, Major Thompson—Bill. A lump came in my throat.

"All right—Bill."

"You're assigned to kitchen duty. But wash up after I've gone. Let's go out into the sunshine and do a little chinning."

We took the boxes we had used for chairs and set them just outside the door.

"Would you believe it, Ned, those damn rats have got that bread I threw out. With us right here!"

"God, I can't stand them!"

"Don't worry. I'll have screens put on the windows and door, today."

For several minutes we sat without speaking. It was warm and sunny. Bill handed me a cigar, held a match for it, and lit one for himself.

"What are you thinking of doing about your family?"

"How can I think? I don't know what is to happen to me. I don't know whether there is any hope of cure. As soon as I get my bearings I ought to send for my brother Tom, I guess. He is my assistant in the business. You had better tell me the truth, Doc—Bill. Don't mince it. I want to know what I'm up against."

He had a funny little twist to his eyelid, like a half wink. You got the idea you couldn't be so bad off when he looked at you like that.

"Look here, Ned. I'm not going to lie to you. I'm not going to fill you up with a lot of bunk. I just don't know a hell of a lot about this thing. Leper bugs I've seen my full share of, because I am interested in bacteriology. In the Philippines I went out to the Lepers' Home at San Lazaro to get material for study. I saw lepers but I paid little attention to them. It was the germ itself I was curious about. A Norwegian named Hansen discovered this particular bacillus nearly forty years ago. We know what it looks like. It is what we call an acid-fast. Under the microscope it looks like the tuberculosis germ. As for hope—well, I didn't lie about that. There is a new treatment; they are using it out there. What the results have been I do not know. I suspect that this is a disease like any other disease. In the past it has been looked upon as hopeless, but I am certain there must be light cases which recover without treatment. You are healthy and strong. If you get treatment you may have a good chance of recovery. I must tell you, though, that this is only my opinion. Actually I know very little about it."

"What about my seeing people? You don't seem scared!"

"Well—I am taking precautions. But I understand enough about leprosy to know that of the many doctors and laymen working with it rarely has one been infected. The public and most of the medical profession knowing little about the disease naturally have a fear of it. . . .

"Now as to your brother. When he comes it would be better to talk with him, with everyone in fact, through or over the fence. Then there can be no danger. With me it's different. I'm your doctor."

"Suppose I say 'to hell with it,' and skip?"

"Not a smart thing to do, Ned. You just can't take the chance of spreading infection. Furthermore you would cut off all chance of help for yourself. You had better stick it out here while we see what can be done. Any ideas you have we will consider, I promise you that."

He was right. I needed Bill. Friendships are queer things. I had met him the day before; yesterday I had wanted to kill him!

"Bill, I can't understand why doctors know so little about leprosy."

"But," he said, smiling, "you are probably the first case in this city. We medicos learn about diseases from working with people who have them. There are a number of lepers in this country. But the total is small, possibly less than a thousand cases. In the United States the disease has never spread as it has in many other countries. Even in Europe it was widespread during the Middle Ages. Personally I think there is a lot of unreasonable fear concerning leprosy. That fear will never pass until we know exactly how the disease is transmitted from one person to another."

"Did many of the soldiers out in the Islands get it?"

"I don't know about that."

"How many have you seen or heard of?"

"Only you."

That hit me hard. "Why should I be picked on?" I muttered. "There must have been seventy-five thousand men who served in the Philippines. I lived as clean as I could, a damned sight cleaner than many of them. Seventy-five thousand men—and I get it! What kind of justice is that? Not a doctor I have seen, except you, had ever seen a leper. Oh yes, Watkins had seen one, just one. What in hell am I to do if nobody knows anything about it? Good God, man—maybe I've already given it to people! Maybe I've infected my own family, mother, Tom, Jane—"

The thought was so hideous it stopped me. I got up and

walked away. I was shaking all over. After a time I went back.

"I'm sorry, Bill. That idea just came to me."

"I think you need not worry about that."

After a while he began talking again.

"You've been a soldier, Ned. So have I. We fought, even I did actually fight at times, for a cause. We believed that Cuba and the Philippines ought to be free. But we began another fight. While the American army was still in Cuba, yellow fever broke out and took a terrible toll. An army surgeon, Dr. Walter Reed, and his associates declared war on the disease. They were working on a theory advanced by a Dr. Finlay, of Havana. Finlay believed that yellow fever was not due to filth conditions, as many thought, but to the bite of a mosquito. One experiment after another was tried, even on members of the medical group, all without results. One night when Dr. Lazear and Dr. Agramonte were studying the problem, a private soldier, Trooper William H. Dean, offered himself for an experiment, and in five days he had yellow fever. Dean eventually recovered but later Lazear himself was bitten and died. They had finally pinned it on a mosquito. She was the carrier. But, Ned, what I want you to know is that it was a private soldier who first proved that Finlay and the others were right. And we are starting to wipe out yellow fever. We've started on malaria and on diphtheria and we've advanced a long way on smallpox. Still we are only beginning. Eventually we are going to conquer them all!

"Now here is this strange thing called leprosy, thousands of years old. I don't know how many millions have it today, but it has taken its toll year after year. We are going to wipe it out some day, put it where smallpox is now.

"Reed, Lazear, Carroll, Agramonte, Trooper Dean, fought in the same war as we did. They took on an extra fight, and won! It may be that you, Ned Langford, are to play a special role in the war against leprosy. Man, if you could have a real part in that fight it would be worth ten ordinary lives like yours and mine!"

He paused, waiting.

"I'm no hero and I don't want to be one," I told him. "When I nearly ran into that Lepers' Home I was scared stiff. I never got to have the slightest hankering for Mauser bullets. When our stables burned I was dead afraid, but I had to go to the horses. I tell you I did what I did because I had to. I haven't any hero stuff in my make-up!"

Bill's eyes held mine. There was that infernal half winking that made him seem amused. After a while he said, "You have to do this, soldier, whether you are scared or not. You can take it standing up fighting, or you can lie down and let it beat you. And you're the only one who can say about that."

There was a long silence. Inside my head the wheels were turning again and they kept grinding it over and over: "You have to do this, soldier."

Over, and over, and over. Then I looked at him. "Yes, I see, Bill. I guess I must. What do you want me to do?"

"I don't know yet. But I have thought of three things you might mull over after I go. It is possible that you could stay here. The Board of Health might allow you to build a small, comfortable house, but I don't believe you would like it here. You run the risk of newspaper publicity if they ever got hold of the truth and it would be difficult to keep you quiet for a long time.

"Then you might go to the Louisiana State Home for Lepers at Carville. I think they would take you. I don't know the place except by reputation, but it seems that the patients are well cared for. The difficulty there is that you are a strong, active man and may remain so indefinitely. You need occupation. At Carville, there is not much work."

"I can't stay here with these rats, or go to Louisiana. Both places are too near home. I want to keep this thing from my folks. Tom will have to know. But I want to get away off."

"Well, you know about Culion. You like the Philippines. Culion is a fairly large island. The colony is under the direction of the Philippine Health Service. That means good doctors, and doctors with a wide experience, since, as I understand it, they have thousands of patients."

"But, suppose I did want to go. Could I get out there? No steamer would carry me."

"In all likelihood no steamer would, but an army transport might. . . . Probably it could be arranged. On the other hand, treatment in this country might be effective. I'd rather you saw another man before going so far. There is a doctor in New York city who has knowledge of the disease. He would tell you just what you would have to do to stay there. If you stayed it would mean great loneliness, but maybe a chance that you wouldn't have to go to Culion at all."

"But it will not be easy to make the trip. I suppose you wouldn't want me to go on a train?"

"No, it would be better if you didn't—"

"We have an old car that we no longer use. It will run. Tom might bring it up."

"Fine! Couldn't do better. I'll write to him tonight."

I gave him directions for reaching Tom and with that he drove away.

I was too tired and my hands were too sore to clean up much, but I boiled the dishes. The night before I had just sprawled on the bunk as it stood. So I straightened the mattress and blankets and made my bed. After a while, some men came and put up the screens Bill had promised me. As soon as they left, I swallowed the doctor's dose.

I went to sleep thinking, "I never thanked Bill."

Breakfast over, I started to clean up where Bill had left off. The place seemed to have collected the dust of ages. At the end of two hours of hard labor with soap and brush and broom, everything was as clean as I could get it. I went outside to smoke and let it dry. When Bill drove up I asked him to go in and have a look. He took it all in and grinned.

"So you have come back to earth. I wrote your brother yesterday and he replied by wire this morning. He will get here day after tomorrow."

"What did you tell him?"

"Just that you were ill and must have a long rest. But Ned, I want to tell him before he comes out here."

That was sparing me.

"Bill, I've never thanked you. I went to sleep thinking I'd never thanked you. I don't know why you're sticking 'round but I'm one grateful guy."

"Nonsense, don't be an idiot. I like you."

"Two days ago I wanted to kill you."

"Yeah, I saw it. Don't blame you. I wasn't exactly kind to you that morning! Come on out to the car; I brought a few little things."

He went to the car standing outside my fence. I stood inside while he passed over a bundle of books, magazines and newspapers. Then he came through the gate carrying a heavy square package which he put on the table.

"Open it. I hope you like it." I tore off the wrappings. It was a small phonograph and a dozen records.

"See here, Bill, this is swell of you. But you mustn't spend your shekels on me. You're doing enough."

"Pff, didn't cost me anything hardly. Have a friend in the business and he practically gives 'em to me. How are the rats? The screens ought to have done some good. Haven't seen any? That's better than I hoped."

Bill remained about an hour, keeping up an incessant chatter. Finally he said, "Well, I've got to operate. I'll bring out some supplies. See you tomorrow."

As soon as Bill had gone I tore the string off the bundle of newspapers and began reading. There wasn't a word about me. I glanced over the magazines, set up the phonograph and began to play the records. About four I realized that I had forgotten dinner. Although I had little appetite I fixed something.

Two days afterwards Tom came. I could see the main road from the fence and I watched the old bus following Bill's car. Bill drove straight past but Tom turned into the lane. When he got close I was startled. Tom looked sick.

He was dead white and his eyes were sunken and hollow.

He got out and came to the fence and we stared at each other. His voice was weak and husky.

"Ned, this is terrible. We have all been worried. And now—it's horrible."

I would have to cheer him up! I could hear Bill's even tones saying over and over, "Soldier, you have to do this—"

"Where's Bill—Major Thompson? Where'd he go?"

"He had some errand. He said to tell you he'd be out later."

"How is everything?"

"Everything is all right at the office. Mother isn't any too well. I brought some letters—" He took a small packet from his pocket. There were three from Jane.

"I'd like to read them."

"Sure, I want you to." He walked along by the fence. I read her letters. In those three days I had gone over it again and again. Was it possible I was never going to marry Jane? Never to see her again? Suppose I was "cured," what was to prevent the thing coming back some day? A bottomless gulf was opening, a gulf that I guessed could never be bridged.

Jane's letters cut deep. They were all about us, the house, and June, and the wedding. I called Tom. I thought he had been crying.

"See here, Tom. Get yourself a box over there to sit on." He brought out some cigars, took one and gave me the rest. We sat on either side of the fence and smoked and talked.

"Ned, you know I'll do anything I can. Dr. Thompson said something about New York."

"Yes. There's a man there who might help me. I wanted to drive the car because it's simpler to go that way. If this New York doctor can't do anything, I'm going back to the Philippines."

"But Thompson says you may get well—"

"See here, Tom, let's not kid ourselves. I did plenty of that for months, wouldn't even think the word. As if that could help! I've got leprosy. Don't look like that. I've got it, and we've got to face the fact."

For quite a while he sat with his face in his hands. Poor boy! I wished I could spare him. But someone had to help me, and there was no one else. Finally he looked up at me. His eyes made me think of a young fawn our dogs had run to bay on one of our hunting trips. I remembered how Bill chattered and chattered, and I went on quickly.

"I'm going to New York and the miracle may happen after all. I've had three days and nights to work this out. I will need your help, Tom."

"But what am I to tell them at home? What am I to say to Jane?"

"Tell them I am dead."

"Dead? I can't do that, Ned. I can't tell mother; it isn't true. I can't tell Jane. I won't tell Jane you're dead while you're still living!" His voice was shrill.

"It's the only way. I'm not insane, you know. Jane has got to think I'm dead. I'd always be afraid, for her, and mother and you."

He saw what I meant. "God, you mean we might, any of us might—"

"I don't know. But I'd be afraid. Bill says it isn't likely

I've infected anyone, yet. But if anyone but you ever knows . . . I can't bear the thought of Jane's wondering if she, too . . . Well, Tom, it's a heavy burden I've put upon you."

"Ned, I'm nearly crazy. You see I'd been thinking. You know, what you told me about Sancho and Carita. I had an idea and I fought it, but it kept coming back. And when you went off I was afraid." He was sobbing now, un-ashamed. I let him alone. Into my mind sprang a wild, fantastic idea.

"See here, Tom. I'll make it easy for you. I'll run the car into deep water somewhere and leave something to identify me. The papers will report me a suicide. You needn't say a word until the news comes, about my dying, I mean."

"Ned, you won't really do that, will you? You won't commit suicide?"

"No-o. I don't think I will. I'm pretty sure I won't. I think I settled that the first night here. I wasn't far from it then. . . . I promise you I am not going to commit suicide now, or in the near future. Did you bring some money?"

"Yes, Dr. Thompson said to give it to him so I gave him five hundred dollars. He'll be along right after dinner. Say, Ned, I brought some food. It's in the car. I'll get it."

He brought a small chicken apiece, celery, paper plates to put things on, some delicatessen salad, buttered bread, and two bottles of beer. He had two forks and two glasses. We ate and drank and cheered up considerably.

We talked about the business and the farms. Then I told him, "I'm going to change my name, Tom. I'm going to be Ned Ferguson. And see here, don't write to me often-

It's a strain on us both. Until you hear from me, write Bill and enclose the letter to me. Now there's just one more thing I have to say."

Bill was driving back up the lane. I had to hurry.

"Tom, take the car to a garage as near here as you can. Tell them you are going away and that your brother will call. Use the name Ferguson. Now don't come back here, but send a messenger with a note telling me where the car is. You'd better give me all the cash you can spare."

While Bill was getting out Tom passed me a hundred dollars in bills.

"I didn't like giving him the money," he said. "But what could I do?"

"Bill's safer than a bank. I just want this in case—"

Bill was lugging something as usual. It was a typewriter!

"Thought you might have some letters," he said gruffly. I put the machine on a box.

"Now, Tom, I can write to Jane. You keep the paper on that side and put it in." I had to take the bandages off, but I managed. It was a short note, telling Jane that I was ill, that my hands were badly infected and that I couldn't write much, and that I was going to New York for treatment. I told her I loved her—and that I missed her as never before. And that was the truth.

Then I asked Tom to go. I looked him over. He was a man now, this brother of mine. We were both pretty tall. He was slim-waisted and lean, as a man should be. I was proud of him. He stammered, trying to say something, but failing.

"Tell it to Bill tonight," I muttered, and that seemed to relieve him.

He turned, cranked the car and went down the road. I stood watching him out of sight.

Bill had taken himself inside the shack but now he came out. As usual he began chattering. When I got to listening he was telling me in great detail exactly what I should do.

"Take the dishes and bed stuff and everything you can pile in," he said. "And then go direct to Todd when you get there. I've sent on four hundred to Todd and I'll leave a hundred for you, here. When you touch money or anything else, wear gloves. It's warm, so sleep in the car nights, or in the open. You've got to wash. Take a can of water with you. Refill from streams or pumps. If you find swift running water, you may take a bath."

"See here, if I do make a bolt, will it reflect on you?"

He grinned sheepishly. "Reflect on me? Man, if you feel your ears burning, you can just say, 'That will be Bill Thompson cussing me out to the Director of Health!'" We talked along.

"Bill, I've changed my name. I'm Ned Ferguson from now on. When you write Dr. Todd in New York, will you tell him?"

"Sure will. That's a good idea. Where'd your brother go?"

"Home. I sent him." He went over my hands, putting on adhesive strips. When he got ready to go it was almost as much of a yank as it had been to say good-by to Tom.

"I'll be seeing you—tomorrow."

"Sure—tomorrow!" I let it go at that.

Tom's note came out in the morning. A young boy

brought it and tossed it through the fence. The car would be ready at noon. It wasn't more than a couple of miles up the main road, and I walked over, brought it to the shack and loaded. Not a soul came near. I cranked up and drove away.

CHAPTER ✦ ✦ ✦ ✦ ✦ ✦ ✦ ✦ ✦ ✦ ✦ SEVEN

IT TOOK ME DAYS TO REACH NEW YORK, BUT I got there. Todd's office was in the east forties. I parked, and went in. I looked pretty ragged. The nurse knew the name Ferguson and took me into a kind of laboratory. After five minutes a man came in.

He was quite unlike Bill and our doctors in the South and West, looking more like a college professor, with his clipped mustache and tiny goatee. But he was helpful enough.

"You want a bath," he stated crisply. "Well, just go through that door on the right." A bath! He was offering me riches!

"Can I bring a bag of clean clothes?" He nodded. I shot down to the car and back again. The bath was a shower. After sponges on the road it felt great! I stuck all my soiled clothes into the bag. The doctor went over me carefully. He kept at one place on my back for a long time.

63

"Now go and dress. Then we can talk." It was not encouraging, that talk. He thought another spot was coming.

"You can stay here for at least six months," he decided, "and see if there is any improvement. Frankly I think the disease is advancing. Do you want to stay?" I said that I did.

"Thompson said that you would. He asked me to arrange for you, so I've rented a little house in Greenwich Village for, as I was instructed, Mr. Ned Ferguson. This place stands apart. You will cook your own meals. Clean your own rooms. You must even wash your own clothes. I've put a standing order with a provision house and the food will be left at your door. If you want it changed, you can phone me; my nurse will take care of that. Yes, the phone is in. There is, of course, no listing. If ever it gets out of order let me know. For money use only coins—and before handling them pour alcohol over them. Wear gloves when you do this and wear them all the time outside. Here is the address. There are some capsules in this envelope. They are chaulmoogra. Take two each day. If they nauseate you so that you cannot endure them, stop. I'd like you to come up here every Saturday afternoon at five o'clock. There will be no other patients here at that time."

He also gave me a brownish liquid in a bottle.

"It is important that you keep your strength. Do you drink?"

"Yes, not to excess, however."

"Well, that's good. Excess of any kind is bad for you. Of course you must avoid all contact with others."

What a cold-blooded specimen he was! The nurse came in—I guess he pushed a button—and she handed me some keys. I got ready to go.

"I hope you'll like the place," he said abruptly. "One doesn't have a big choice. I'd come down with you if I could, but—I'll phone in an hour or so."

I had some difficulty in finding the place and when I did I'll say it was amazing! Over near the Hudson River, a blacksmith and wheelwright had closed his shop. Too many autos coming in. He had lived there in a narrow house less than ten feet wide, a kind of lean-to on one side of the shop. The old anvils and wheels were still inside. The house itself was two-storied, a kitchen and sitting room downstairs with a small hall between. From the hall a stair ran to the two rooms and bath on the second floor. My outer door opened from the hall into a yard, paved for the most part, but containing some bricked flower beds and a tree, the ailanthus tree of the city. The windows, all on one side, faced east. The building next door was low. It, too, had been a shop and was now closed, so there would be morning sunshine. The place was clean and my food supplies were on the step. After I had looked around and decided that the furniture would do, I carried in the food, unloaded the typewriter and the phonograph and some of the clothing. I left the bag with the clothes I had taken off in the doctor's office, in the car. From my pocket I took all the letters Tom had brought me, except the three from Jane, and placed them in the bag. Dr. Todd called me. I thanked him and said my quarters were O.K.

When I got into the car and drove all round Manhattan and over into Brooklyn, I saw that it wasn't going to be as easy as I had figured to stage my "suicide." The city was much bigger than I had realized and there were people everywhere.

At a clean dairy stand I got milk in a bottle. They had sandwiches wrapped in paper, so I bought a couple of them. Refreshed, the hunting began again. At last I found the right spot. On the East River near Harlem stood a small dock with a little-used road leading to it. I went back to my place, satisfied.

At two A.M. I returned. No one was about; streets, road and dock were empty. I drove the car onto the dock and kept the engine going. Then I released the brakes, put her in gear, and jumped out. She went right into the water and turned turtle. A man was running in my direction but he was a good hundred yards off. Quietly I came out on the side away from him and just walked away. No one noticed me.

In the morning I went out and bought a paper, fumbling awkwardly in my pocket with my gloves to get a coin to pay the man. On page fourteen I found the story of my "death." They had the car, had found my bag and the letters with my address at home. The body was missing. The harbor police were dragging, but there had been a strong tide and it was likely that the corpse had been carried out to sea. I felt queer enough at the thought of being a corpse.

I stayed nearly a year in New York. Todd did all that he could, and in the end I got to like him a lot. He may have treated other lepers; I never knew. Indeed, in that whole time I never knew anybody, or about anything not in the public print. There were nearly five million human beings crowded all round me and I did my best to be alone. The subway remained a mystery; trolleys and trains were things to be avoided. I was crazy about baseball, so I used to go to the Polo Grounds on week days and sat upon newspapers I carried out and spread, at the edge of the bleachers far from anyone else. I walked to and from the grounds. It was a great season. McGraw's pennant winners were doing themselves proud, and Christy Mathewson was pitching. The trip was over seven miles each way but it was worth it.

Nights when I could not sleep I wandered through the parks. From Washington Square at the end of Fifth Avenue, up to Central Park at Fifty-ninth Street, and around and across the curved paths. Or along the bright lights of Broadway, gleaming for everyone but me. Men and women in gala dress, going here and there, and laughing. . . .

I think I forgot how to laugh that year.

One day when Caruso was to sing at the Metropolitan I convinced myself that if I got there early enough to be first in line, I would hurt no one. I made it. But they came and came and soon the man in back was pushing me. At once I dropped out. The man behind me stared.

"Here," he yelled. "Wot de hell you go off for? Dey open soon."

That night I wandered back to the Opera House. It was late but on the Thirty-ninth Street side were about a dozen people, men and women, just standing. A policeman stood too, watching. And as I wondered, there came to us a voice, golden, magic. The night was warm, the ventilators were open. That penetrating voice carried out to us. I stood and heard him through. I heard Caruso.

The next day Dr. Todd telephoned me to come to his office.

"Mr. Ferguson," he said, "you are not getting better. I am sorrier than I can tell you."

It would have been a greater shock had I not guessed it all along. I had already made my decision. To endure the loneliness of this great city, to be in it and not of it, was no longer possible.

"Doctor, will you write to Bill? I want to go to Culion."

He agreed and I went back to my house of isolation in the Village. Bill kept his word. He wrote me at once. There was a transport leaving soon, from San Francisco. Could I make it? I told Todd I could, and would. Then I wrote Tom of my decision:

DEAR TOM:

I've reached the end. It's insane for me to attempt to go on longer with this farce. I've clung in stupid desperation to the thought that I would grow better, that I must grow better. I've refused, hour by hour, to believe that such a thing could or was actually happening to me.

For almost one year it has gone on just like that, hour by hour. Yes, minute following minute, every interminable waking minute trying to calm myself into believing that it wasn't happening, that it couldn't happen to me any more than it could happen to you, or mother, or Jane, or Horace Windle or Bill Thompson. Every foot of every block of the city streets that I have paced week in and week out, month in and month out, can testify to the prayers that I have breathed in that unreality and incredibility. Now I'm through.

It has happened, Tom. Incredible as it is, it has happened to me. I'm a leper, a leper who for a solid year has been living in a fool's paradise of make-believe, pretend·

ing that I would once more see home, and mother, Mabel, and you at some time if not soon. Even that some time I would be going back to Jane and that she would not ask where I had been, or why. That together we would finish our house and begin our life.

That's not going to happen, Tom. I'm through. Don't put me down as a quitter. I'm not quitting, actually. Your long and so good letter came two days ago. I do not think you need worry that I shall do away with myself. It is useless to give you the promise you asked of me—I don't believe that it would be possible to know whether it may finally be the only way. I can't say whether I shall always be able to control my thinking. I believe that it will not happen simply because it hasn't happened. I faced it for hours on the banks of the Mississippi that first night. I've barely missed it several times during the last year.

One time I took a steamer that runs from Battery Park to Coney Island. I thought the going down the bay, the music and gaiety, the amusements at Coney would help me to forget for a few hours. They only made me remember all the more deeply. I spent the hour on the boat trying to avoid pressing against the crowd—my actions attracted attention and people looked at me suspiciously. I became confused and embarrassed. At last I found myself on the lower deck at the extreme stern of the boat. There I was alone except for a watchman who occasionally strolled past. Evidently he had grown suspicious, too, or some of the passengers had pointed me out. I was not far from it then, Tom. The white, foamy wake of the ship a few feet below me looked warm and peaceful. You helped me then, kid, just as you have on other occasions. I remembered what you have asked repeatedly. You wrote once, remember: "Don't ever just quit."

I don't want you to have to think that I did quit. I can't promise, but I have really tried like hell not to.

That same night when we landed at the beach I could do nothing. Every amusement meant crowding in with a lot of people. I made the attempt several times and each time had to step out of line. A nausea spread through my whole body. I went back to the boat and when I saw its brilliantly lighted deck, my knees went weak. I couldn't face another agonizing hour on board. I turned back and, keeping in the shadow, crossed to where the lights grew few and although it was miles back to the city, I walked it. Walked and walked through that whole night. I walked, and thought and suffered. You could never believe how alone aloneness is. You have to move, live, breathe, see, hear, in the midst of millions of people, not daring to touch one of them, afraid to speak lest they become friendly—avoiding—avoiding—eternally avoiding.

I can't endure another day of it. I'm going where there are others like me, where there will be thousands of us, where I need not hesitate to speak to the man I meet in the street. Where, if someone jostles me I don't have to slink away from him like a beaten dog.

I've had a crazy passion at times to go up to Union Square or into the theater throngs on Broadway late at night and suddenly scream at those laughing, carefree thousands—"Look, everyone! Look at me! My name is Ned Langford and I'm a man, too. I'm a human just as much as you are. I've even got a girl. She was going to marry me, but I'm a leper—a leper!" I've even laughed at the picture I have drawn of the horror and fear and insane revulsion that would freeze their laughter and send them fighting to get away from such a menace.

And yet, Tom, why would they? Why do people everywhere have such fear of the very word? If you were to see me now you would not think of me as sick. You would not see any change; none of my spots are where they can be seen. Practically the only change is that another spot is appearing. The doctor tells me that the disease sometimes progresses rapidly but that often it is a very slow thing. . . . It's only that it is still alive in me and this year of taking treatment has done nothing to kill it. It isn't humanly possible to go on any longer like this.

I've tried to be careful of other people but I have sometimes forgotten. The first few times I visited the doctor's office I went up in the elevator, and then one day the nurse happened to be coming up at the same time. That day Dr. Todd asked me to use the stairs, and after that I walked up and down.

One night I was sitting on an empty bench in Washington Square—I go there often to sit in the semi-darkness and watch the lights stretching up Fifth Avenue.

It's a beautiful sight, particularly on rainy nights, when the wet pavement is a kaleidoscope under the lights of the hansoms and busses, victorias and an occasional automobile.

I had been sitting there this night for an hour or so— a full moon was over the houses toward the East River. A girl sat down at the far end of the bench I occupied. I noticed that she was shabbily dressed and her thin face looked hard under the heavy rouging. Presently she edged a little toward me. "Good evening, Fella," she said. "Good evening," I replied. She said nothing more for a time, waiting for me to speak, perhaps. Then she said, "It's a swell night, ain't it?" I replied that it was. "Live around here?" I told her that I lived not far, over toward the Hudson River. "Who do you live with?" "No one," I told her. "Gee, that's tough, how about taking me with you."

I looked at her long and intently. She wasn't much for looks but she was alive. She talked to me.

No one had done that for so long. She was a woman,

not much of a woman, perhaps, but a woman, nevertheless. If she went with me there would be a woman in my house, maybe she would laugh, and I would hear laughter —a woman's laughter. My hesitation irritated her. "What's the matter, afraid of me?" The question struck me as very funny. "Afraid of you?"

A policeman strolled by and she fell silent. When he had gone, she said, "You're a queer nut, ain't you?" "Yes, queer." "Well, I don't mind, Bo, guess we all are a little, what say?"

The passing of the cop brought me around. I remembered Todd and the ban of isolation he had laid upon me. "No, I'm afraid that I can't take you with me." "Oh, you are, are you? Can't take me with you! What is the matter with me? Not good enough for you, eh? Just who do you think you are, anyhow? To hell with you"; and with that she got up and walked rapidly away.

Good God, not good enough for me! Even that miserable streetwalker seemed like an angel from heaven. Even she was not alone like I am, not one of those doomed to walk alone. No one fled from her—no one had put upon her the injunction to avoid everyone.

That night, as I returned to my empty house, my spirits were about as low as they were in the shack when I killed the rat.

Tom, there is one other thing I wish to tell you. I have held on to Jane in my thinking, through all this—I just couldn't get myself to believe that she was lost. This must be the end of that, too. Nothing can be saved from the ruins, not even my identity. I want you to look after Jane. If she is ever in need of anything I know you will take care of it.

Before you can reply to this letter I shall probably be gone. Bill is helping me get a transport for Manila—you can write me at Culion. This is the end of my old life. Tomorrow I shall be a part of my new world.

I know nothing of the world into which I am going. When I am there I shall write to you. Meanwhile don't think I've quit. I've just accepted what can't be avoided —I've lost my life—I shall try to find it again.

Affectionately,

NED.

After that letter I was ready to start. I had burned my furniture piece by piece in the tiny fireplace and had cleaned the whole place with disinfectants as Todd had instructed me. Only my trunk, typewriter and talking machine remained. Todd had promised to send these to the transport.

I turned the key in the lock and left.

CHAPTER ✦ ✦ ✦ ✦ ✦ ✦ ✦ ✦ ✦ ✦ ✦ ✦ EIGHT

I WALKED UP AND ACROSS TO ELEVENTH AVE-
nue—"Death Avenue" they called it, because of the railroad tracks. Watching my chance I climbed into a box car.

That trip across country remains in my memory as a
nightmare. Arriving at little stations in the dead of night—
being chased by railroad brakemen—lying huddled in empty
coal cars trying to keep warm—finding food wherever I
could—begging it at farmhouses and being looked at with
suspicion when I offered to pay. Clinging to the rods, de-
bating whether to hold on longer with my hands numbed
from the cold, or let go. Avoiding tramps who insisted on
becoming friendly. Toward the last, living in fear that I
would miss the transport, I who had money in my pocket
with which to purchase every comfort that the fastest trans-
continental express made possible! But there was always the
danger of infecting someone else. This way, at least, I didn't
have that on my soul.

74

I arrived in San Francisco the day the transport was to
sail and went at once to the dock. A soldier stopped me at
the gangplank.

"Where you makin' for, Bo?"

"I'm sailing on this ship."

"Oh yeah?"

"I am! They expect me."

"Sure, they expect Mutt and Jeff too. On your way, bum.
This is a boat for soldiers."

"I know it's a boat for soldiers. I was one once."

"Well, once ain't now."

I was desperate. It could no longer matter who knew.

"I'm a leper."

"You're nuts."

I lost my temper.

"Tell Dr. Sidney that Ned Ferguson is here."

Seeing that I knew the name of the ship's doctor he
looked at me with a curious expression of incredulity. He
fell back several paces and called the guard standing at the
head of the gangplank.

"Call Dr. Sidney."

A moment later an officer appeared wearing the insignia
of the medical corps.

"Ferguson?"

"Yes, sir."

"Come aboard."

As I started up I saw the guard cross himself. I barely
caught his words, "Jesus, Mary and Joseph!"

"I'm glad you made it. I had begun to get a little worried. I'll show you to your quarters."

He took me to the cabin where I was to remain in seclu·

sion. It was small but comfortable, and had its own bath-room. There were letters and parcels from Tom and Bill. I let them lie. I unpacked my clothes. My hair was a mess. I knew I had a hard job ahead of me. In New York I had been my own barber, but on the road I let it go. So I waded in.

A bugle sounded. From above came the tramp of march-ing men, and music. The scissors fell. Fifteen years ago I had made this voyage—on deck. There had been more than a thousand men on the old *China*; there were a thousand on board now, a thousand and one—me. My hands were not steady enough to cut hair while the tramp, tramp, tramp went on. But when it stopped I made good progress. As I finished I heard the engines. I hurried to a porthole and opened it. The shores of San Francisco Bay began to slip by. That wonderful harbor was going, going; we were passing through the Golden Gate. I believed that I was looking for the last time on the shores of home.

There was a knock at my door. It was Dr. Sidney. He was a twinkling kind of man with a shining bald pate on top of a short, fat body, neat as a pin, in his late forties, a jolly soul. He began to laugh.

"Good heavens, man, I never saw such a change in a human being. Had to cut it yourself! You made a good job of it!"

"Thanks a lot. And, Dr. Sidney, just make it 'Ned,' will you?"

"I'd like to, Ned. Now for your routine. Meals will be brought to your door. You'll have to wash your own dishes; the water from the faucet is very hot. I'm afraid that I will be your only visitor, although the captain wishes to come as far as the door to speak with you."

"He's welcome."

Despite Dr. Sidney's visits, the hours seemed endless. My letters and parcels helped to fill in my excess time. I was pleased to find that the talking machine and typewriter had arrived safely. In Bill's letter he told me he knew one of the Filipino doctors very well, a Dr. Ravino, and he had written him. Tom had sent some records; also a brief letter. Poor Tom, he had a hard time writing letters at any time, let alone to me. Mother was well again, Mabel had married. Her husband might come into the business. Jane had gone to Cleveland to teach in a music school.

Several days later Captain Robinson came to see me. He bade me welcome very formally and extended his best wishes. I was wearing a white suit. He appeared both surprised and pleased at my appearance. Evidently he had expected little of a leper.

That afternoon, while playing the talking machine, I suddenly began to feel sick. It was unlike anything I had hitherto experienced. Nausea and burning. I grew quite dizzy. Struggling out of my clothes, I discovered the spot on my leg was inflamed. The places on my arm were also reddened. Wondering what had hit me, I dropped into my bunk. When Dr. Sidney came in, he said it was a puzzle to him.

"You've had a lot of excitement. A weaker man would have collapsed in a day or two after a trip like yours. Just keep quiet and you'll come around."

He left me some medicine that kept me quiet all right. I slept and slept. In a few days I was back to normal. Months later I found that I had gone through my first "leper re-action," one of the curses of this disease.

As I convalesced I began to enjoy my new records. The title of one selection was not familiar, but as the orchestra played a few strains, I gradually recognized it. It was my song, our song—Jane's and mine. It had been altered a little, there was a minor passage that had not been there at first. Jane must have done that. I was back in the old life, wandering with Jane, riding with Jane—the flash of her gray-blue eyes, the toss of her head. Planning our home to-gether—the needle was scraping. I shut the thing off and sat with the disk in my hands. The door opened.

"What's the matter, Ned? Sick again? You're as white as if you'd seen a ghost."

"I did," I muttered.

Dr. Sidney was an understanding kind of fellow; he made no reply.

It took about a week to reach Honolulu. Some of the men were to disembark there. From my cabin I could catch glimpses of the harbor and the islands about. We laid by a day. The men bound for Manila had shore leave, and I could see them coming and going.

Three weeks more, weeks that stretched to infinity! There were hours when I paced the little cabin like a caged animal and other hours when I sat and brooded, head in hands, and grew morose and sulky. Then Dr. Sidney would come, with a new batch of yarns—he saved up every joke for me—and I would snap out of it.

When we came into Manila Bay I was sorry that my cabin was on the portside. I would like to have seen the rocky fortress of Corregidor and the bay itself. On my side one could follow the ragged shore line with its dense tropical growth. We came alongside to starboard so I could not see the pier but just the boats on the bay. The regimental band struck up and I heard the tramp of men marching off. Then I waited.

That was one of the worst times I put in. Hours and hours passed. From noon to late afternoon, I sat in the stifling heat. I relived my first landing fifteen years before, when I was an eager youngster anxious to do his part in setting the world right. Again I was going ashore to fight, this time without drums or bugles, to fight a foe I would never see.

Dr. Sidney came in at the end of the long afternoon. He had been busy, he said, and did not realize how the time had passed. He told me that a health officer would call for me. He knew no more of the arrangements.

"Ordered supper for you, Ned. It is so late you might miss out on it altogether. They will be along any time now."

Supper was just something to do. I had no appetite. It was almost dark when Dr. Sidney brought a Filipino into my cabin.

"Mr. Ferguson," said Sid conventionally, "this is Dr. Ravino, Major Thompson's friend. Dr. Ravino is Chief Clinician out—where you are going."

Dr. Ravino bowed with great formality. He was a short, slight man, part Spanish, I guessed. He was not only courteous, but diffident, almost shy.

"I am truly sorry, Mr. Ferguson, that you return to

Manila with this misfortune, after serving your country out here. I assure you that we will do all we can for you."

I thanked him. He told me to pack just enough for the night and that someone would call for my things later. Then we started. The two doctors preceded me through the corridor. When we came out into the open I could see only a blank warehouse wall, the gangplank, and a part of the ship's rail on which a half dozen sailors were leaning. They looked around, startled. I heard one gasp:

"Oh, my God! There's that leper!"

As one man they left the rail and hurried off. Dr. Ravino had taken my arm and swung me around. He was asking,

"Do you recall the bay? How beautiful it looks under moonlight?" But he had not been quick enough to prevent my seeing the look of horror and aversion that swept across each face of the six.

Dr. Sidney, too, spoke quickly. "Some day I'm coming to Culion, Ned. This isn't good-by. And I'm writing Bill."

"I hope I will see you. Thanks for all you have done for me."

As we walked the length of the pier I wondered if I would ever see him again.

CHAPTER ✦ ✦ ✦ ✦ ✦ ✦ ✦ ✦ ✦ ✦ ✦ ✦ NINE

D<small>R. RAVINO HAD A CARROMATA WAITING.</small>
The little pony cart looked familiar, and I was reminded of
old Juan. The doctor stepped aside and allowed me to go
in first, as if I were a visitor of importance and not just
another patient for him to care for.

"San Lazaro Hospital."

I wondered if this was the "Leper Home" I had seen that
day during the Insurrection? I asked a few questions and
found that it was. Our cochero flicked his little Spanish
pony and it trotted, trotted. Blindfold I should have known
I was back in Manila. Nowhere else had I heard that quick
plop-plop of tiny feet. The little beasts are forced to trot
the very life out of their short legs.

It was now quite dark. But I could catch glimpses of a
new city springing up on all sides. The old moat and the
swamps about the walled city were gone. Parks were beginning to appear where formerly there was only filth,

stench and decay. The bay itself was being pushed back by new-made land and between the old walls and the shore there was a splendid new hotel flaming with lights. Houses and buildings were going up all along the bay side of the Pasig River. We clattered across the beautiful old Spanish bridge, and then time turned back. Again I was in old Manila. This side was much as the American army had found it.

It was quieter out here and Dr. Ravino began to apologize for the long wait on the transport.

"We thought it better, Mr. Ferguson. There were a number of new patients who came in today and they all had to be examined before allowing them to enter the wards. We check on patients without regard to previous examinations. Many of our men in the provinces, who have been sent there as health officers, have had little experience with the disease. You would have found it most unpleasant with all the commotion and disturbance. Now it will be quiet."

"You mean you will examine me tonight?"

"Oh, with you it is different. Major Thompson sent us a few slides with smears." So Bill had kept that under his hat!

"Major Thompson worked with us during the time he was stationed in the Islands. He is a good bacteriologist and we do not feel that it is essential to examine you bacteriologically. If you are willing, we should like to make a simple routine examination—just to keep our records clear."

"If I were willing." He knew as well as I did that I had to be willing. But a Filipino is polite first and last and always.

"Certainly," I muttered. "Anything you like."

"You will find it very crowded at present in San Lazaro.

You see, we bring patients here from all the islands in this vicinity and at intervals the government puts a boat at our disposal and we remove some of them to Culion. Because of this situation we are unable to do quite as we should wish for you. I trust that you will understand and know that at all times we will do our best."

"That is why I wanted to come here," I replied. "I knew that you would do your best. But I want to be treated just as the others are. No special favors."

That seemed to please him. He changed the subject.

"As an educated man, you will find San Lazaro a place of interest. For over three hundred years it has been a 'Sanctuary of Sorrow.'"

A "Sanctuary of Sorrow"! This clinician must be a romanticist. The moon was climbing above the old Spanish houses. In its white light the city took on mystery. Out of the deep shadow of the carromata came a tale; the voice went on and on. I forgot why I was there. I forgot where I was going. There was something rhythmic in the man's tones, spaced with the plop-plop of the ponies' tiny feet.

"The year Drake made his voyage around the world, Sir Francis Drake; in that year of 1577 there came to this island men of the Order of St. Francis. To the convent, where they lived, the beggars came each day, waiting hour after hour outside the walls for their almoner, Fra Juan Clemente. He was a lay brother who waited upon them. He saw that many were lepers. What spiritual growth began within him no man knows, but he begged his superior to help him build a shelter for these unfortunates. In time he was told he might have the land in front of the convent. It was swamp land on the edge of the Pasig. But Fra Juan

Clemente was not discouraged. He enlisted the more able bodied of the lepers and they with him carried sand and soil from the river to fill the morass. In time the land was firm and then they built a few houses, nipa and bamboo. And they called the place for Lazarus, whom Christ made whole.

"Fra Juan Clemente went the way of all men, but his spirit survived. San Lazaro had been wiped out by fire, but it was rebuilt outside the city walls. Then it was deliberately destroyed as a military measure against threatened invasion by Chinese pirates. The King of Spain became interested, and with the aid of royal subsidies, a beautiful new stone building rose on the same site, this time accommodating several hundred patients. For over a century this hospital flourished. Then fear of an English attack again caused its demolition by the Spaniards. In 1784 San Lazaro was once more rebuilt by royal order of the King of Spain. It has endured since, although fire and plague have both attacked it. In the early seventeenth century when the feudal system of Japan was coming into its ascendancy, many Christians were banished from that country. The ruling powers of Japan agreed to send to the Islands of his Christian Majesty the King of Spain a company of one hundred and thirty-four converted Christians. His Christian Majesty the King of Spain accepted them. A few months after their arrival all but four were admitted to San Lazaro as lepers."

We were turning in at the wide gates in the stone wall. I was to become a part of that Sanctuary of Sorrow, with its memories of over three hundred years. The pony had stopped. We got out. I followed Dr. Ravino down a corridor into an office.

"Unfortunately, Dr. Kent, our American director, is away on an inspection tour. If you do not mind, I, myself, will examine you. Just where are your lesions, Mr. Ferguson?"

I told him.

"If you will remove your shirt—"

He went over me, touching the spots with something sharp, and asking me to keep my eyes closed. Then he repeated the touching, this time using a feather.

"I am sorry," he said, "the early diagnosis is quite correct. But do not be discouraged. We are giving a new treatment and there is a chance it will benefit you. It may be slow, but we could not have promised you a chance a few years ago. Now, if you please, your record."

That took some time. I fumbled over family, residence, and so forth. Finally I told him the truth, that I was using an assumed name and that my family, all but my brother, believed me dead. He said he understood.

"Now, I'll show you where you are to sleep." We entered a long, narrow room. Single wooden cots were along both walls, all occupied. . . . A cold sweat started on my forehead and a current swept through my head and down my spine. Two or three of the men stirred but no one spoke. My bed was nearest the door and a great open window admitted a soft breeze. I noticed that it was the only one with a mosquito net over it. I protested to Dr. Ravino. "You must not favor me. Please have the net taken off."

"But it is necessary," he explained. "Our people are hardened to mosquitoes. We have little malaria now, but they would bite you. You would not sleep. Everyone will understand."

I mumbled thanks and, when he had gone, crawled under the netting. Hours after I was still staring out of the big window. From the room came the sound of heavily sleeping men; two or three moaned and tossed. They didn't disturb me, what was worrying me was why I was there at all. I, Ned Langford, a leper, sleeping with a roomful of lepers! Why hadn't I died when I pretended to die? Well, I'd die yet; there would be chances. The sea, that was it, the sea!

Somebody was sobbing. It sounded like a child. I raised myself on one elbow. Just across from me was a figure smaller than the rest. I lay back again, hoping the sobs would cease. But they kept on and on, softly and incessantly.

I couldn't stand it. I slipped from under the netting and crossed to the bed. He was just a youngster lying face down muffling his sobs in his arms. Putting out my hand to touch him, so as not to frighten him, I sat down on the edge of the bed. His body tensed. His sobbing grew quieter as I patted his shoulder. He turned to look at me. The moon was bright and I could see him clearly. A fine looking lad; my heart went out to him.

"What is your name?" I asked him.

"Tomas, sir—Tomas Aguilar."

"How old are you, Tomas?"

"Ten, almost. It's much more than nine, sir."

"Where is your home?"

"Very far from here—more than fifty kilometers. Too far for the carabao to come."

"When did you come?"

"The doctor, sir. He bring me from my home today."

Between slackening sobs he went on to tell me that it was the first time he had been away from home. He spoke of his father and mother, his two older brothers and a sister —a baby. It was his mother and the baby whom he missed most.

Light came while I sat there. He had come close to me and snuggling over against my shoulder had gone fast asleep.

IT WAS FULLY LIGHT WHEN, ROUSING FROM A doze, I opened my eyes to find the man in the next bed staring at me. I was sitting propped against the wall and the sleeping lad was still snuggling against me. As I came to consciousness I saw the stare replaced by a wide, friendly smile.

"Good morning, sir. You are Mr. Ferguson?"

"Good morning. You know about me?"

"Oh yes, sir, Dr. Ravino told us you would be coming in late. Paco! Paco!" he called to the next bed where another man was stirring.

"Paco, this is Mr. Ferguson. I am Manuel." With that he rolled out of bed and came over with outstretched hand. It was a year since I had shaken hands with anyone. I hesitated, remembered, and shook hands. I could not harm him. The fact sent a wave of relief through me.

Almost at once the whole ward was astir. All the men

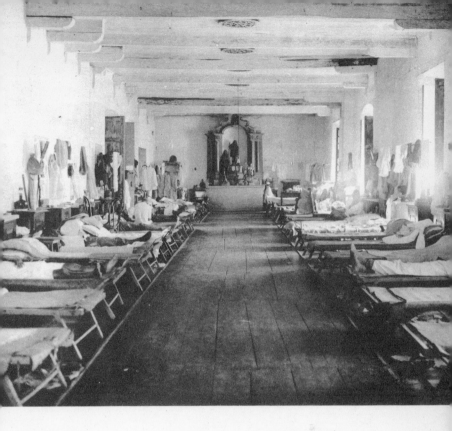

San Lazaro dormitory.

rose—there were evidently no severe cases here. Several of those nearest came to my bed to welcome me.

"I hope you had a good voyage, Mr. Ferguson."

"Did the boy disturb you? That is too bad."

"No," I replied quickly. "We were both awake and we just got to visiting and I dropped off to sleep sitting here."

But Tomas had wakened and hastened to contradict me.

"Excuse me, please, sir. I did disturb him. He was highly kind to me. I wept and he came and talked with me and he made me feel happy again, and I went to sleep against him. I make very serious thanks to you, sir."

Tomas was kneeling on the bed and looking at me with so much gratitude in his big, brown eyes that I was taken aback. What I had done was very little. But the Filipino is devoted to his family, and the fact that I had fathered the lad for a few hours won their hearts and their friendship. My explanation that I wasn't asleep was smiled aside.

"That was indeed kind of you, sir," said Manuel. "We should all be ashamed to you that we have let you do what we should have done."

The ice was fairly broken. I had dreaded the moment when I should meet lepers as lepers. But all that was past. We were kin, not strangers. As we went to the mess hall I found those of my own ward gathering about me. I had a feeling that they were protecting me from seeing some of the more advanced cases. There were men here who were disfigured. I had no appetite for breakfast: fruit, rice and stewed fish. Again they were kind. I was asked whether I would prefer eggs, but I assured them that I had eaten and liked Filipino food and would eat whatever was served.

There was a great current of excitement among the patients. Manuel, at my side, explained:

"It is because the boat for Culion is expected soon. For me, I want to go to Culion. It is a good island, there will be much to do. But some of these who are here fear going, because they may never return to their families."

I thought of my own home, of mother's sweet face. I felt a little sick.

"I can't get there too quickly," I managed to answer.

At breakfast on the third morning, slips were given to us all, notifying us whether we were to go or remain. The boat had come and would sail the next day. There were about two hundred to go, and my name was among them.

Relatives and friends of the patients had been notified, and by noon the barriers that kept visitors from entering the hospital, were crowded. I couldn't stand it long. Mothers and fathers, wives and husbands, talking frantically, hour after hour, trying to crowd into that time what might have been said during the remainder of their lives. When night came and they had to leave, their pitiful cries rang in my ears. I was glad that was over. I could not sleep the whole night.

But it was not over. The next day as we boarded the Coast Guard cutter, the pier was filled with people, who cried to their relatives as we crowded the decks. A few of the patients fell fainting. One badly crippled and shockingly disfigured old woman crumpled up on the pier when the attendants tried to make her walk up the gangplank. A young girl, her daughter, no doubt, rushed forward from the crowd of well people to assist her. But the police held her back, gently enough. One of the patients ran down the gangplank, gathered the woman up in his arms and carried her aboard.

When the lines were cast off and we began to turn away, wails of anguish from decks and pier rent the air. Many were in hysterics. On the pier I could see police forcibly restraining frantic souls who would have thrown themselves into the water and swum after us. Some of the lepers on deck tried to throw themselves into the water, and the doctors and nurses in charge were put to it to prevent them. It was bedlam.

Tomas, at my side, was shuddering. He did not cry, but he kept swallowing hard. Poor lad. He had explained to me carefully that his family could not come to say good-by. They lived too far away; it would have been a long journey for their carabao. He watched anxiously to see that I believed him; he did not want me to think that they lacked affection for him. I assured him that I understood.

Culion lies less than two hundred miles south of Manila. I could not understand the impression of great distance that gave the separation an added terror. But, as I was to learn, the chances of visiting were slight because of the infrequent trips of the boats, which poked their noses into every little harbor along the way. For many, even the few pesos charged for passage made the visit impossible.

During the twenty-four hours it took us, going direct with no stops, to reach our destination, I was told over and over: "I shall never again see home, friends or family." A number of the patients were terrified of what was to happen when they arrived. As a leper colony, Culion was not ten years old. Previous to its founding, a few hundred of the more advanced cases had been confined in hospitals near their homes. The lighter cases had remained at home. In the back provinces there was no isolation. When Culion was opened and the Philippine Health Service forced people to go to the island, there was great resentment. Frightful stories of torture and abuse were passed about. At the time we went down the truth had gradually become known, but there still was great fear among a large number.

It is said, and I think it is the truth, that there are few places in the world more beautiful than the tropical blue waters and the thousands of coral islands of fantastic shapes, cloaked in deep green, that stretch through the sea for hundreds of miles south of the bigger islands of the Philippine archipelago. Mangrove swamps, beginning at the water's edge, are lost in wide expanses of coconut trees that sweep up to meet the wild jungles rising above them.

Tomas and I sat on deck watching. There were few cabins on the little boat and the patients had their quarters on the two decks. The lower deck was narrow and near the water; the upper, far more spacious, was hot, protected from the scorching sun by a soiled and weather-worn canvas. We ate, slept and walked, when we could find space, on this deck.

As we went down the bay a tall American doctor came up and spoke to me. I learned, to my surprise, that he was the United States Director of Health for the Philippine Islands. He rattled it off without ceremony and gave me his name, James Marshall. He was a man in his late thirties, slender and lithe as an athlete. He wore a Palm Beach suit and a brown sun helmet. Life appeared a continual frolic to him, for his eyes danced and he smiled at slight provocation.

Never have I met a man who was keener about his job. He was in his eighth year on the Islands.

He sat near us and looked over the deckload of patients. "I like to go down with this boat when I can. This is our new battlefield. You know we have banished a number of plagues here. Cholera and smallpox have almost gone. With this disease of leprosy we have had a hard time. When the Americans came, there were hundreds of cases roaming the streets, maybe thousands, and about four hundred in hospitals and institutions. It has been difficult to get patients to go to Culion. But there is their hope—for recovery."

I started: "For recovery?"

"Yes, Mr. Ferguson, for recovery."

My backbone felt stiffer. He spoke with such assurance I began to believe there might be a chance. He had gone, but I hoped I might see more of him. Certainly he had a way of putting heart into you. He came with these boatloads; the Director of Health would hardly be required to do that. He risked infection. . . . I gave it up.

Just before suppertime we entered Calavite Straits, running between the islands of Mindoro and Lubang. The water was rough. As the ship began to roll from side to side, one passenger after another went to the rail. The odor of food rose from the galley and further complicated matters. Dr. Marshall came back.

"We might seek a less crowded spot," he suggested with a grin. "This is a regular occurrence. Suppose we go forward on the lower deck."

I looked around for Tomas. He was curled up in a corner

fast asleep. We went down the short companionway, then forward to where the ship's rail turned in to separate the mid and forward decks. No patients were expected to go in front of that rail. I stopped. He raised the wooden bar of the barrier.

"Come on. We can sit on the hatches. Usually I eat with the captain but sometimes they bring supper to me down here. It will come along pretty soon."

I sat down on the end of the tarpaulin-covered hatch and he dropped near me, making no effort to keep a distance between us.

"See that island over there?" He pointed to the portside. "That's Mindoro, one of the largest of the Philippines. It stretches almost as far south as Culion. Most of the interior is unexplored. Hunters like to go there to find the tamarau, a sort of ox, wild and undersized, known nowhere else in the world. It is ferocious and dangerous, since it attacks without provocation and is difficult to kill. Few men have succeeded in bagging one of those animals and many have lost their lives in a vain attempt."

He went on and on, and I listened, fascinated. In his work he had traveled repeatedly from one end of the Islands to the other. I began to see the Philippines as a treasure, rich in natural products of timber, minerals, hemp, rice, coconuts, fish. He liked the Filipinos and he expected great things of them in the future. A boy brought supper to us on trays, American food, largely from cans. It tasted fine after the few days of native food. I did like the native food, but not as an exclusive diet.

I told him something of my own life. The sea, lapping at the sides of the boat now that we had reached calmer waters, no longer tempted me. The last few nights its call had been almost a command. But under this man's enthusiasm, courage mounted.

"What we need most," he said, "is steady and unremitting co-operation of patients. We can't cure without that."

Without speaking, I pledged him mine. Then he spoke of other patients and I told Tomas's brief history. Marshall called the boy who had brought supper, and sent him in search of Tomas. Presently a shy head stuck around the forward cabins and when we motioned to him, Tomas came and sat near us.

Later, when it was quite dark and the stars hung so low they seemed within pistol shot, we three stretched out on the canvas and tried to sleep. The doctor went off promptly; Tomas and I lay there awake for hours. Tomas dropped off at last but I remained sleepless, my second night without sleep. Yet I was not done up. Certainly I was still in good shape physically; there might be a chance. The top of the mast swung slowly back and forth, back and forth. I wondered whether it would spear one particularly bright star directly above the ship. I wondered about Marshall, what success a man like that could have, stuck away off here. I wondered lazily, and although I did not sleep, I knew the first real relaxation in a year. The die was cast.

The doctor awoke at dawn, said he had some people to see but that he would be back to breakfast with us, and for me to stay put. When he came back he carried a pitcher of water and a bowl.

"Crowded back there," he said. "We can have a little wash up here." He had washed, however, and it was Tomas and I who made use of what he brought. On the starboard side there was land, and directly ahead was a great green headland partly hidden by clouds.

"This island on your right is Busuanga," said Marshall, "and the headland is the northern tip of Coron. Coron runs nearly down to Culion. It is almost unexplored and largely inaccessible. We run through the narrow passage between these islands—see, we have headed west—and then we swing around Coron which tapers off much in the way South America does. And then we shall sight Culion."

We stood at the rail. The ship was close in to shore. Towering rocks rose straight out of the water to a height far above the mast of our ship. The sea ran between the two islands like a mill race and was beaten into foam against the jutting rocks. Then the whole of Culion Harbor appeared.

For the moment I forgot what the place meant. I drew a deep breath. Miles of the most beautiful harbor I had ever seen. It was almost landlocked. Straight ahead the dim outline of Culion itself; to our left Coron stretched its great length; Busuanga on the north and west ran almost to Culion. Hundreds of little islands formed a broken barrier between the harbor and the China Sea. The sea was gentian blue above its coral bed, rimmed about by tall green islands. And vast—there seemed ample anchorage for the fleets of the world.

"I'd better get back to my patients now," said Marshall. "I like to be with them as we near the Island. We do our best to check the silly stories about it, but they are apt to result in some hysteria. Sometimes people try to throw themselves into the sea. Stay here if you like."

He was off. From the deck we could see an almost round, tall hill rising sharply out of the water. There seemed not a foot of level ground. On the east point I could make out a high promontory with a light above it on the walls of what seemed an old fort. Towering above the walls, but within them, there was a large stone church. As we came nearer, the hillside broke up into terraces, level spots one above another, and on these and stuck against the sloping hill I could see the thatched roofs of hundreds of small nipa houses. Here and there were larger buildings of stone or stucco, hospitals, administration offices, maybe.

The water of the harbor was dotted with many dark objects, which, as we came nearer, proved to be scores of small boats, outrigger canoes or rafts, crude things made of pieces of bamboo lashed together. On these rafts two or three people would sit and paddle. From a short distance they appeared to be sitting on the water. Each boat carried some kind of colorful decoration, a strip of bright paper fastened to an upright stick, begrimed flags—flags of the United States and the Philippines. Atop the tall flagpole on shore I was able to make out the two ensigns, my own flag flying above the other.

The engine bell jangled. Speed was cut to half and then slow. Finally we were drifting into the ring of small craft. It was clear that this was a welcoming flotilla from the colony. There was a rattle of chains as the anchor was dropped, and we slowly swung toward the shore fifty yards beyond. A hand slipped into mine. I looked down. I had forgotten Tomas. Never had I seen such an expression on the face of a child. His eyes were fixed on the shore. There was bewilderment, aloneness and fear in those dark eyes.

I pressed his hand and he sent me a quick, wondering, upward glance.

Suddenly I was glad of that small hand. We were not alone; there were two of us.

CHAPTER , , , , , , , , , , ELEVEN

As soon as we had anchored, a large flat-bottomed boat something on the order of a scow was pulled alongside by a motor launch, made fast to the ship and a gangplank was let down. We were opposite Balala, that portion of the settlement which was reserved for doctors, nurses and the well people of the administration. The scow was to take us patients around the point of land at the old fort to the pier of the colony proper. There was no safe anchorage for the large boat except in the deep water of the main bay. As the crowd began to load itself and its baggage onto the scow, Marshall stopped by.

"I'd wait till the last trip if I were you. It will not be so crowded. I will be going then, and we can arrive together. Have Tomas wait with you."

Then he was off again and I could see and hear him among the patients, helping and encouraging them.

As soon as the first of them started down the gangplank

they were hailed by cries and much waving of hands from the water craft. Evidently many of them had friends already in the colony. The little boats, bancas, and balsa rafts crowded in close to the big scow and a few men actually tried to climb the sides, impatient to join relatives or friends. As the scow started, a number of the smaller craft promptly paddled after it, thus forming an escort. I could now see that the promontory was topped by a pole bearing a lamp, much on the order of a street light and it was toward this that the scow proceeded, rounding it and disappearing. Boatload after boatload followed. Dr. Marshall came back.

"Next load is the last one," he advised us.

"So many of these people seem to know others who are already here." I was puzzled.

"Yes, that is quite in keeping with leprosy as we know it. Anywhere leprosy exists it seems to have fairly definite foci. We do not know why that is true. Possibly because, once having a foothold, the chances of infection are greater. But why it first picked on certain spots is still a mystery. There are provinces here in the Islands where there is a great deal of the disease, and an adjoining province will have very little. That may be true even between barrios. In the United States there are only about four states where leprosy is endemic, and in those states it is chiefly confined to a few definite areas. I have seen a residency in Java where the disease is heavy and an adjoining one practically free from it. In Puerto Rico most leprosy is found in a few towns and in one of those at least, mainly in two streets. You can see that it is logical that every boatload coming here should carry people who will find at Culion someone known at home. I am glad that it is so. It makes it so much easier for the newcomers, and it brings news of home to those already here."

He talked to me as if I were a visiting doctor, not a patient with the disease well started. So far as he was concerned, I was not set apart. We were not set apart. There was no separation. This busy man with the welfare of millions in his hands, knew mankind as a whole. Its afflicted were just a part of mankind. And his sympathies were just as active toward them as though all were his personal friends. He was glad, "that it was so." I believed him.

As we ran along by the shore I could see the small nipa houses occupied, he told me, by patients. I saw a road winding through the coconut and mango trees. Above the road the hill rose sharply. The doctor indicated an upper road, invisible to us, far above the first one, and pointed out houses along both roads. We ran under the rounded high point and turned into a smaller, inner harbor. Halfway up on the right there was a wharf jutting out into the water. A crowd of people stood on it, waiting, evidently for this last lot of us.

"You were in the Islands long enough to know how hospitable its people are. There will doubtless be a reception when we land."

That struck me as decidedly odd. We, the banished, were to be welcomed to the company of the banished! It didn't seem exactly an occasion for rejoicing. But these people in Culion thought otherwise. As we came alongside the wooden landing stage, men in uniform were shooing the crowd off the wharf and to one side. Our fellow passengers from the boat were drawn up in a long line on the left.

"The police are patients," said Marshall. "You see we quarantine new patients."

"For leprosy?"

"Oh, no. But for other infectious diseases. Leprosy rarely kills, you know. It is some other disease that carries off the patient in almost all cases. And a leper may contract any other disease. If he does not, he is apt to live out his normal life, especially here where he is well cared for."

The boatmen were easing us into the pier and making fast. The passengers hung back for Dr. Marshall, but he waved them on ahead, and then motioned to Tomas and me to go ashore. He came last. As he stepped to the wharf a string band struck up a lively air. We followed the others and slowly got into line. To my great amazement a reception committee was there to welcome us. First came the Medical Staff, the Chief of the Colony who was an American, and a group of Filipino doctors, all wearing white surgeon's gowns. Following them came the nurses, and others I could not identify. The Padre, the Roman Catholic priest, was also gowned. There were two groups of nurses, one in the habit of the Sisters of St. Paul de Chartres, and the other, the regular nurses of the Philippine Health Service. After greeting Dr. Marshall they turned to the long line of patients and went along, speaking to each one. I was amazed as each doctor came by with a greeting to every new patient. Dr. Winton, the Chief of the Colony, a tall man, hatless and white gowned, stopped with me for several minutes.

"You look very fit," he said. "Well, it's an ordeal. But don't let anything you see get you down. I wish I could skip this quarantine for you; we'll see later. I'll be back before noon if I can manage it. I have some suggestions to make as to your quarters. I'll have to ask to be excused now as I have all these others to care for."

I mumbled thanks. He was keen and brisk like Marshall, and his gray eyes looked straight through you. But he was much younger, younger even than I was. What a job for a young man!

The Padre was approaching and he stopped a bit too. "My name is Marello, Mr. Ferguson. We are sorry that you must come here, but we all hope you will find some happiness."

It came to me that he might know about Sancho.

"Have you a patient here by the name of Sancho Nolasco?"

"Oh, yes—he is in the hospital. How is it that you know him?"

"I knew his family when I was in the army. Could you give him a message for me?"

"Certainly, my son."

"Then tell him, Father, Sergeant Ned is here and will come to see him as soon as he can."

They cheered us up quite a lot with a simple program of short speeches and more music. Certainly we were all made to feel welcome. I stole a glance at some of the doubting Thomases who had circulated the horrible yarns about Culion. They looked puzzled. Perhaps they thought we were being fattened for the lions.

When the ceremonies were over we filed into a large building that served as a quarantine station, women on one side of a partition running the full length of the place, men on the other. There were canvas cots and a few bowls for washing. Food was brought from a general kitchen. Tomas and I took our share, which was nicely wrapped in banana leaves, and climbed up a steep bank near by. Here under a grove of papayas, we ate in picnic fashion. We were still at it when I heard a voice from above.

"How are you making out? Did they give you enough to eat?"

I looked above and saw the Chief, Dr. Winton. He was slipping and sliding down to us. He had shed his white gown and appeared dressed informally in a short-sleeved white shirt, open at the throat, tan riding breeches, and high tan riding boots.

"Sorry I couldn't make it earlier. There's always so much to see to when a boat comes bringing so many. What I wanted to talk about is a place for you to live. You see we are always crowded and it's a job to get everyone located. We have few general dormitories. Most of the patients build their own small houses; four or five of one family, or those who are friends, go in together. The colony furnishes materials and tools and they do the work. This boatload means two hundred additional to house and it takes some doing.

"Now for you. There was an American here—I will tell you his story some day. He died of tuberculosis a few months ago. When he was dying he asked me to see that his house went to some other American. He built it, so I promised, and it has remained empty ever since. If you want the place it's yours. It is well located and planned differently from the Filipino homes. You could have the place to yourself."

(top) *Balala. This is the area in which live the well people of Culion. The radio tower and the pier are in the center. Church Hill, which is within the colony section, appears immediately beyond the tower in the middle right.*

(bottom) *The colony along the inner bay side, looking toward the interior of the Island. The new (upper) road from the colony to Balala is visible along the center of the hill.*

(top) Some of the patients' houses, overlooking Culion Harbor. Across the harbor is the island of Busuanga.

(bottom) The inner bay as seen from a section of the colony. Many of these houses are the homes of fishermen.

"But what of the others?" I asked. "I'm going to live here and don't want to arouse antagonism as the recipient of special favors."

"You need have no fear on that score. That house is known as 'the Americano's' and they would think it strange if you did not take it. The fact that you alone occupy it would arouse nothing but pity. The Filipino is a gregarious individual; he does not want to live alone. And he is not jealous. All the residents know that Wilkinson built the house and that he left it for any one of his own people who might come here."

"It sounds like a great bit of luck for me."

"H'm." He smiled a little. "I wouldn't go that far. The place is pretty well run down—he was sick for some time, in the hospital for months in fact. I tell you, come along now and let's have a look at it. If you like it, okay. If you don't we will talk again. But perhaps you had better stay there until you get ready to build for yourself."

Tomas, with the native diffidence of the Filipino, had withdrawn to allow us to talk, and Dr. Winton turned to him.

"Tomas, will you wait for us a little while? Mr. Ferguson will come back to you."

Tomas obligingly curled himself up to take a siesta. We clambered straight up the steep bank, at times almost crawling on hands and knees. I learned then and there that Winton never took the long way round when he could find a short cut; hence his rough-and-ready attire. Before long we came upon a road which he said was a branch off the main one and ran on the right to the hospitals and administrative buildings. We turned left. There were many paths leading back over the hills.

"Paths but no roads," said Winton. "They lead into the interior, as yet barely touched."

We sauntered along at an easy pace. Heavy borders of coconut palms and banana trees, with flaming hibiscus in full bloom, lined the sides and gave us shade. Here and there we came upon a small cleared space and a house of bamboo and nipa. For the most part such houses were built on high posts so that the single floor was at second story height. A slanting ladder or crude steps provided means of ascent. Underneath the house a few chickens shared quarters with a mangy dog or two. We saw few human beings. Those we passed greeted us with smiles.

"Good afternoon, Doctor," and then with a polite nod to me turned away. One man squatted in the shade was patiently exercising a fighting cock. There were a number of small shops, bazar-like affairs where candies, cigarettes, cigars and a few trinkets were sold—tiendas, they were called. The swali shutters were all closed.

"Siesta time," said Winton. "I never take one. The place is full of shops like these. Of course none of them make much money, but they do give the patients something to do, and idleness is a problem here. The Chinese do exceptionally well. They are born to trade, the Chinese."

"But are the patients fit to work?"

"Most of them are perfectly able to do some work, not under pressure, of course."

I thought of that year of torture in New York. It had taken me a few hours a day to do the essential things for my living. Then despite walks, baseball and reading, how long the hours had been!

"I want to be as busy as possible, and I am in good shape."

"If you hanker for work you can have enough, I assure you. But you will have to find it for yourself. We don't serve it out with food tickets, although I don't know why we don't. It might be a good idea. Here's your layout. Come, let's have a look."

He pushed open a rickety, wooden gate which was set into what had been a fence of split bamboo, now pretty well wrecked. Plants and tropical undergrowth completely obscured the house. We pushed our way through the tangle and I saw that the building stood some fifty feet back from the road.

"I am sorry we didn't get in and clear up a bit for you. But although you may wonder how, this Island near runs me ragged."

"I wonder you can spend so much time on me," I answered. "You have twenty-five hundred people, I am told. Patients, I mean, not counting the well ones."

"We did have. You birds flew in and raised it to twenty-seven hundred."

I noticed he avoided the issue. This fellow was all right. I liked him.

We had come to the front steps and he started up. He broke through the second step, a nasty fall. He was up before I could give him a hand.

"Are you hurt?"

"Yes, my pride's bruised horribly. Here am I, Chief of the Colony, showing off, and the house lets me down. You will have plenty to do if you take this wreck, Mr. Fer—oh, let me call you Ned."

"Please do."

I had seen the bay and it made my throat catch. No matter if the whole place had tumbled down, I wanted that location. The grounds ran down to the water, at least Dr. Winton said I could have all that if I wanted it. My predecessor had been too ill to bother. The house was the usual nipa and bamboo. It was rectangular, twenty by forty feet. On the road side and running the full width of the house was a general living and dining room, which was also a porch. The shutters of swali—woven nipa—opened outward and upward with hinges at the top, and when propped open made the room practically part of the outdoors. Behind this were two small bedrooms with a hall between, which ran into another hall across the house, separating the bedrooms from the kitchen and a small room which seemed to have been a storeroom. There was no bath. When I asked the doctor where Wilkinson had bathed, he pointed to the bay.

There were two iron bedsteads, a collection of stands and tables, chairs and benches. In the kitchen we found a rusty oil stove, pots and pans, much rusted, and a motley assortment of china, chipped and cracked.

"It looks worse than I figured," said the doctor. "Leave a thing like this alone and how it runs to seed!"

"We can very easily clean it up."

"That's fine. Well, if you like it so much, you may observe your quarantine here. Just stay in until it is lifted, I mean in the grounds. I'll have your stuff sent from the boat, and I will send out new mattresses, bedclothing and food."

"You mean I can stay here from now on?" I hated the idea of that quarantine shack.

"Sure. Now, there is something else. The boy Tomas. Dr. Marshall says you have an interest in the little fellow. Why not have him come here with you? He could be your house boy. If you have money you can pay him a very little. I think he would be glad to come if you want him."

I felt the pressure of that small hand in mine. Two of us.

"I'd like it more than I can tell you. Tomas is a fine lad and I've taken a fancy to the little shaver."

"Then that's settled. I'll send him up to you."

He had gone. I was alone in my new home. I went about the grounds again and when I got back from the bay Tomas had arrived and was waiting for me.

"He—the Chief, Dr. Winton, says I am to stay with you. It is so?"

"Yes," I assented. "Say, Tomas, we have a house but it's kind of shaky. Look out where you are going! Dr. Winton is sending some supplies to us. Maybe we can fix that step so we can get them in. Meanwhile you scurry around and see if you can locate some drinking water."

He found a tin bucket and disappeared. Our stuff came with surprising promptness and we were hard at it the rest of the day. That nightfall saw us fairly well settled. I was dead tired. For three nights I had hardly slept and this day I had worked. Tomas and I got supper together. He would not eat with me. He set my supper on a small stand and retired to the kitchen.

I sat there smoking. The soft tropical night was all about me. The stars were mirrored in the still waters of the bay. It was just pleasantly warm. I yawned. Then I got myself to bed and slept.

THE PATCH OF MY WINDOW WAS TURNING
from black to gray when I was rudely awakened by the
most outlandish burst of crowing I have ever heard. Years
before I had been accustomed to this characteristic morning call in country barrios of the Islands. But nowhere had
I ever heard anything that compared with this. Every patient on the Island must own a fighting cock, and the fra-
ternity have a secret understanding to turn on the works
simultaneously. It spoiled sleep for that morning. But I had
enjoyed the best eight hours in weeks so I jumped up to
see how the boy had fared. His room was empty.

"Tomas! Tomas!" I called, drowning out the cocks.

"Yes, sir, I am in the kitchen, sir." His voice was weak
and muffled. Hurrying in, I saw him before the old oil
stove, down on his knees.

"Oh, I make very sorry excuse to you, sir. I cannot make
the stove to burn and many good matches I have completely destroyed."

I dropped onto a chair and laughed uproariously, partly with relief that Tomas was still with me, and safe.

"Look, Tomas, see that little thing there before the burner? Turn it to the right. The wicks are turned down, that is all. Now hold your match against that wick; there, you see?"

The boy rose and stood looking at me mournfully.

"I am very abundantly ignorant, sir. I think that soon you will send me away."

"Don't you believe it, Tomas. Why, you and I are pals. You know what a pal is, don't you?"

"Oh, yes, sir. I know that. A pal is a bucket to carry water in."

"We call that a pail, Tomas. My kind of pal means a chum, a friend, someone who goes about with you and shares your troubles and even some of your secrets, someone you like a whole lot, almost as much as your own family."

His face lit up.

"You mean we can be like that, sir?"

"Why, we have already begun, Tomas. We began way back in San Lazaro. And the Chief says you may stay here with me as long as you wish. Oh, we shall be, as you say, abundantly pals, Tomas."

"You—you are very kind, sir—" His voice quavered. But the kid had the real stuff; he kept right on—"you are good and I make many thanks." There were tears, unshed, in his big dark eyes. "P-please to excuse me, sir, I forget the water." He grabbed a tin bucket and ran out.

Poor little tike, torn from his mother and his baby sister. I was a poor substitute, but he was clutching eagerly at my offer of friendship. When he came back with water I told him what an American breakfast meant. I was a good cook after my year in New York, but never having had the task of breaking in one, I was a trifle indefinite. I did not stay to supervise. I took some of the water and went to shave.

He set me a place in the living room on a small stand and put before me a large bowl of fruit, yellow mangoes and papayas and green bananas, that variety which contradicts itself by being green when ripe. I did not inquire where he got them. Some, I felt sure, came from our own trees. The rest, perhaps, had not. . . . Then he brought the eggs. I waited until he had gone and tested one. It was gray and hard as lead. Tomas on that morning set a standard never equaled. I fired the first egg at a dog snooping around the porch. He howled and ran, and the egg rolled into some bushes. The second I tackled, but gave up quickly and put it into my pocket. Tomas, returning, saw no eggs, not even shells. He grinned broadly as he set down the coffee.

"You like eggs, sir. Maybe some day I become very good cook." I was so full of laughter that I gulped the coffee and nearly choked. It was full of grounds! Tomas watched anxiously.

"It is not okay, sir?"

"Oh," I coughed, "quite. Only my taste in coffee is peculiar, Tomas. I like it clear. Come, I will show you." We cleared the rest of the coffee with a little cold water and I managed to drink it.

It was about ten o'clock and we were working on the steps when Dr. Marshall came up through the brush.

"Hello!" he called. "Working already! I heard that you

liked the place." That was all that was needed to make me garrulous. I began planning aloud. I would do this and that. He seemed much interested.

"You can get almost anything in Manila. If you have difficulty, have Dr. Winton write me and I'll try to see that it is sent. When I come again you will have done wonders to this place, and I shall look forward to seeing them."

He had been, as Tomas would have said, abundantly kind to me. I watched him go with real regret. His straight back and squared shoulders, even the vigorous wave of the hand as he turned down the road and caught me standing watching, were gusty with life.

In the afternoon I had another caller, Dr. Winton. He came out by the side of the house dragging a chair with him.

"Well, you are making progress. Fine work. Before I forget it, this chair is just another of our little customs. Callers are permitted, as you see. But we try to keep the chance of infection down to a minimum. Well visitors may not be served with food or drinks; if they wish they may bring their own. This chair came from the small shed back there. Have you looked into it?"

"Tomas and I peered through the small opening. The door was shut so we did not go in."

"The things in the shed are supplied by us. When a guest comes he fetches his own chair and replaces it when he goes. I observe this rule and so do the other doctors. Naturally the patients never touch the chairs; if they need repairing or replacing, just inform me.

"I'm concerned about your food, Ned. The colony issues food tickets, but you will not want to live upon native food alone. You are not accustomed to it, and it is better for you to keep mainly, for some time at least, to an American diet. I do not know what your financial resources are, but it will cost only a little to get what you need. Tomas will draw his rations from the colony stores; he will want his own kind of food. See here, have you a pension?"

"No, I never applied. There was no need." But—if anything happened to Tom . . . "It might be a good plan to apply, although I am here under a false name and haven't the ghost of an idea how to go about it."

"Oh, we could manage all that. Nothing would need to be made public. Your record is right here. I have an idea you might get seventy-five dollars a month, one hundred and fifty pesos. That would go a long way toward helping you fix up the place and you could pay the boy something and feed yourself."

"It puts you to a lot of trouble, Dr. Winton, but the money would be welcome. My brother has been supplying it, but I'd like to stop that. I have several hundred with me. By the time that is gone, perhaps the pension will arrive."

"I'll attend to the application, then. Do you know about colony money, no? We have coins of our own. To make your American money good you have to change it for this special coinage; it is all metal, no paper. This is done at the Colony Hall; anyone can direct you. Now let us get to groceries and so on. You must tell me what you like."

Together we made out a long list, and he left to get the order off, as the boat was going back that day.

"I'll send you some supplies from my own stock until yours come. And, I almost forgot. Father Marello said that he would call as soon as your quarantine is over."

I thanked him and he swung off at a fast clip. How those doctors did go—and in all that heat!

The next morning he sent down a number of tools and we got to work with a vim. We fixed up doors and shutters, patched furniture, and cleared paths. We kept at it steadily for days. Tom had sent some new books with the lot of stuff that came to the transport and I hadn't finished them all yet. When I was too tired to go on, I sat on my porch and smoked and read, or listened to the phonograph. It was curious how out of key I felt with the books. I was reading "Sister Carrie," which had made such a furore in America, and just didn't care a continental about Carrie or any of the other characters. I laid the book aside as someone called:

"Good afternoon. May I come in?" Father Marello had come through the little gate and was standing on our cleared path.

"By all means," I said eagerly. "I have been hoping you would be along soon." He turned and went around the house and came back with one of the chairs. He put it on the porch, sat down and removed his hat. It was hot—and I could not offer him even a drink of water!

"You see I know my way about," he said, smiling. "Wilkinson was a member of my church. This is one of the coolest spots on the Island, and"—he was looking about—"how you have worked! Why, the place looks made over."

"This is the beginning, Father. There is much more to be done."

He looked at me quizzically. "I might ask a blessing on the undertaking. It would please Tomas, at least."

I could have kicked myself for forgetting Tomas.

"Father, Tomas has worked like a carabao." He chuckled, for I had substituted that hard-working beast for our "beaver." "Father, you must want to talk to Tomas. I'll call him. And when you bless the undertaking, I'd like to be around."

"Don't call Tomas, I want to find him myself. And it is good of you to attend even so simple a service of a church not your own."

He went off, taking the chair with him. After a time, Tomas, his great eyes shining, came for me and we walked down toward the shore. On that spot Father Marello called a blessing on the sea which was never to trouble us, on the land which was to be fruitful, on the house and its inmates, that we might find peace and rest within its walls. It was a wholesome and broad blessing and both Tomas and I felt uplifted. Then Father Marello and I went back to the porch and his manner changed.

"Would you care to go with me to the hospital tomorrow to see Sancho? Dr. Winton thinks we had better go early, before visiting hours. So many come then."

"Of course I'll go—I want to go. How is he getting on?"

"I am sorry to tell you that he is one of our advanced cases. You see Sancho is tuberculous. That may be the reason why his condition has progressed so fast. He has little resistance to the disease. I am afraid it may not be a happy visit for you. He thinks he has infected you."

"But that is nonsense, Father. We campaigned all over the Islands. There is no reason to suppose that I was infected in his house. I must talk with Sancho." There was something else I had to know. "Father—Sancho had a sister —Carita—"

"Yes, my son. She also has leprosy. The disease flared up in her when her baby was born, as so often happens."

"No, no—not Carita! No, I tell you! . . . Where is she? If she is a leper why isn't she here?"

"She was teaching at Concepcion up in the country and they sent her to the leprosarium at Cebu."

"Is she—is she like Sancho?"

"No, my son. She is nothing like Sancho. You must not take it too hard. It might have been worse."

I laughed and it was not pleasant laughter.

"Might have been worse. She is a leper and you tell me it might have been worse! That sweet pretty little girl, that good girl—where was your God that He didn't know she was good?"

"We do not know the ways of God, my son—"

"The ways of God," I shouted. "What a God, to turn His face the other way on children like Sancho and Carita. Do not preach to me about such a God!"

He waited.

Suddenly I felt abashed and fell silent. He did not speak. Finally I mumbled, "I am ashamed of myself. You are a guest in my house." He smiled, a faint, weary smile, but a patient one.

"And I have just blessed the house in the name of my God. The blessing stands. And I continue to sit here. There is no offense."

I could stand no more. I got up and walked to the window and stood looking at the unkempt garden. He waited a long time. I did not hear him get up but I felt his hand on my arm.

"You will be sore tried at times, my son. I felt you had to know before we went tomorrow. Good night and the peace of God be with you."

I stalked back to the kitchen, got a bottle of whiskey from a shelf. Regulations or no regulations I had to have a drink. I took the bottle back with me. Tomas came in with my supper but I could not speak to him. He saw the whiskey and understanding came into his eyes. He went away softly. A guttural voice outside kept calling me, calling me. I started to answer and then began to laugh. It was a gecko, one of those large lizards that frequent Filipino houses.

The dogs began as they did at dusk, barking and howling. They were followed by a more horrible howling from the wild dogs outside, the marauders which came down from the hills to prowl about the cemetery. I took up the bottle and held it to my mouth. I was going to get out of this horror by the easiest road.

I was very drunk when I fell asleep.

To TOMAS'S DELIGHT, THE MORNING FOUND me fit as a fiddle. I sat on the porch waiting for the Padre, and when I saw his white robe between the trees, I went down and joined him.

At this time of day before the sun reached its maximum, the road was much traveled. As I had little inclination to talk, I employed my eyes. All the passers-by were cordial to us. Some said good morning, others were shy and just nodded and smiled. They were a picturesque lot. The men wore transparent white shirts of piña, a cloth made from the pineapple plant, and wore them with the tails hanging down outside their trousers of white cotton. Some shirts were colored. They were shod in white sneakers; a few wore straw sandals; some went barefoot. The women were gorgeous in multi-colored, native dresses, also of piña cloth with huge starched sleeves standing out like butterfly wings. They were decked with trinkets, glittering earrings, necklaces ending in religious symbols, bracelets and rings. Their gay slippers, usually bright red or blue, were embroidered on the toes with silver, gilt or colored beads. There were children of all ages. It was depressing to see so many very young ones.

We took a zigzag road to the left and followed it for a short time, until I stopped for a view from a high point of vantage. We were on a hill. Directly below us was a public square, the Plaza, with stone buildings flanking it upon two sides.

"Plaza Libertad," said Father Marello. "The stone buildings are the first dormitories which were built. They are very crowded although they accommodate so small a proportion of the colonists."

The square was fairly full of people, particularly near the dormitories. There was a continuous passing to and fro from small sheds in the rear. Father Marello said these were used for cooking. We went on, downhill this time as the road dipped sharply. We passed a building on the right, then a large, open general kitchen which prepared food for those in the hospitals. On the left, at the turn, stood a fine two-storied structure of stone, in Spanish style, with a pillared portico running its full length.

"The Colony Hall," remarked the Padre. "Here are the post office and the general stores. Some of the food is distributed here. On the upper floor, court is held. You must attend court some day. The accused may have their own lawyers, chosen from among colony members. The Chief acts as magistrate and hears the case."

We were entering a wide road, evidently the main one. To the left it led from the colony proper to the area reserved for the well people, and to the right it curved around the point where stood the Catholic church and the harbor light, and down the hill to make the lower road we had glimpsed from the boat.

Just ahead of us was a long flight of wooden steps, hundreds of them it seemed, built among the trees and shrubbery. This was one of three flights used as short cuts between the two roads. Up and down toiled men and women. Many carried heavy loads, the men suspending them from the ends of long sticks balanced across their shoulders. The women carried their bundles on their heads.

It was growing very hot on the road and the steps looked cool and inviting as they were practically tunneled among the trees. I had never seen most of these people, but here again, chaperoned of course by the Padre, I was welcomed. It may have been because of him that my welcome was so warm, but it was directed to me. I wondered at the smiling faces. This morning I had a feeling there was nothing in life worth smiling about. After a time I stopped and drew a deep breath. A break in the trees gave a long view of that magnificent harbor.

The blue water was stirred by the monsoon and broke into little crests of white foam. Far to the upper side was the line of Busuanga and toward the east the corroded sides of picturesque Coron.

A little farther on we came upon a group of women washing clothes. The Filipino loves cleanliness. To maintain husband, herself and children in the immaculate attire they all love, Filipino wives must spend a large part of every day at laundry work. They make a fiesta of it, a group of them working together. Here the garments were placed upon a stone slab and the "lavendera," squatting, mechanically beat them in a slow and regular rhythm, with a heavy, smooth stick of wood. Just beyond we turned from the highway to a small path running to a long, single-storied building.

"This," said the Padre, "is the General Hospital."

My knees went weak. A sweetish, sickening odor came through the open door. For the first time I was going to see what leprosy could do. Here were the heavy cases, and thus far I had seen none as bad as these must be. We went through the door into a corridor and from that to the ward. It was a long narrow room much like the ward at San Lazaro. On both sides were windows of Capiz shells and on the bay side glimpses of the sea were visible through the trees.

I followed the Padre, keeping my eyes resolutely glued to his white robe, not seeing anything else until we stopped beside an iron cot. The figure that lay there was covered to the chin with a sheet.

"He is almost blind." I was repeating what the Padre had told me, repeating it as if it would help me not to see what I beheld.

Never in my wildest imaginings had I dreamed of horror like this. This—this rotting piece of flesh was not Sancho—Sancho the fine-featured lad I had known, riding the family water buffalo down to the creek for a bath, exercising his father's fighting cocks, playing merrily with the other children. . . .

He had not moved. He lay there and I looked. His eyebrows and eyelashes had gone; his forehead was covered with shiny, reddish welts, some of which were open wounds. The bridge of his nose had fallen in and the nostrils were widely distended and frightfully swollen with great festering tubercules. Through those ulcerated cavities the air was sucked audibly into his lungs. His lips, like his nostrils, were thick and enlarged and a paralysis of the mouth was beginning, so that it was set in an immobile, open oval.

The Padre, watching me, spoke:

"Sancho, my son, I have brought someone to see you."

The flesh moved. The eyes, opening, turned toward me. He spoke, but I could not understand; his voice was weak and there was a queer and terrifying hoarseness, sepulchral. . . . I was being addressed by the dead. I looked at the Padre.

"Is that you, sergeant?"

If I could talk, it must be quickly.

"Yes, Sancho. I came as fast as I could. I was in quarantine, you know."

He moved his head. I went on talking. I had to. I reminded him that I had heard that he believed he had infected me. I assured him with vehemence that it could not be so. I repeated it two or three times.

He was trying to speak. I stopped to listen. He tried to thank me and to smile. That was the most horrible thing of all. Then a change came over his body, it began to twitch and somehow I knew he was crying and muttering he had infected Carita. The Padre touched my arm.

"Come," he said. As we went a nurse came to the bed. Through her soothing tones I could hear Sancho's moans, pitiful, weak, helpless, hopeless.

"Carita—Carita—Carita."

The tears were coursing down my cheeks. Mercifully they blinded me so that I did not wholly see the figures in each bed, but I saw enough. As we neared the door, a man was sitting by his bed. He had no hands; there were bandages where the ends of the stumps came. One foot was uncovered, to be bandaged. The whole thing was a mess of festering flesh. A figure in white was kneeling, just by. It rose at our approach—it was a woman, Sister Victoire, the Senior of the little group. She smiled sweetly at us. She had the face of a saint.

"Good morning, Father. Good morning, Mr. Ferguson."

She was going to bandage that foot! I dashed past the Padre out into the underbrush where I was violently ill.

I had no clear recollection, ever, of the trip back to my house. I got there, for after a time I found myself alone on the porch with the whiskey bottle beside me. I drank deep and was sick again. The miserable day wore on. I drank and was sick, and drank. After a time I looked toward the sea. It had called me. I took a deep drink and started unsteadily toward it. But I could not walk and I fell into a chair. Tomas was standing by me, calling, calling, calling.

"You are sick, sir. I call and call. I am much afraid. I speak and speak to you many times and you do not make answer. I fear very much you die. Then I would die too, sir. Since I lose my mother and father and my brothers and my little baby sister, you are for me all. If you must die, I must die also."

The last drink stayed down. I could hear and understand. At once revulsion swept me. I heard the Major—"You've got to do this, soldier." I shook a dizzy fist at the sea. Not yet—there was plenty of time. Carita—I might be able to help. Sancho was taking it—to the end. Tomas, literally kneeling at my feet, lifted his dark terrified eyes to me. I put an arm down and raised him.

"I'll be damned if you are a better man than I am, my little Malay brother. Yes, I shall be damned if you are."

A few days later I learned that Sancho had died that night.

CHAPTER ✦ ✦ ✦ ✦ ✦ ✦ ✦ ✦ ✦ ✦ FOURTEEN

WHEN I WAS SOBER I DID WHAT WAS PER-
haps the first real thinking of my life. I had to have a plan
of living, otherwise this running amuck would be the end
of me. And that was not the kind of end I proposed to
have. All morning I pondered it over while I wandered
about the house and grounds, restless, and unsatisfied. I
was no longer horrified. I accepted what I had seen. I was
a strong man still and needed something to occupy my
mind.

But what could there be in a place like this for a man
to do? Everything was provided—food, clothes, medicine.
What reason to work and what opportunity?

A boat was in from Manila and Tomas had gone to the
Colony Hall on the chance that there might be letters for
one or both of us. I was down by the beach when he returned. There was a stranger with him. He was the Protestant minister, Mr. Hudson, who had just arrived and was

to remain a few days before returning to Manila. He came forward a little anxiously and looked me over. I suspected that Father Marello had told him of my visit to Sancho.

"I'm mighty glad to see you," I told him.

We visited for several hours. He came from Kansas and we felt neighborly at once.

"How would you like to go with me tomorrow for a motor boat trip around the islands?"

"I'd like it fine," I said.

"All right. Meet me at the colony pier right after lunch."

When I arrived he was waiting. He had brought a boat around from Balala.

We ran out of the inner bay, and along the shore of Culion. Ahead of us was a group of many small islands. We went in and out among them until we reached the open China Sea. There was only an occasional nipa house on the shores. These islands were a part of the leper reservation; a few lived out there and went in to the colony once a week for treatment and food. Most of them traveled back and forth on bamboo rafts. They had small fish traps near their homes.

On our way back I was impressed by the strange beauty of Coron.

Deep ridges cut the whole length of its tall and precipitous sides. The constant erosion of sea and wind was forever at work changing the broken surface of stone. Huge broad-limbed trees had found a way for their roots in the sparse soil. This alternation of disintegrating massive rock with the green of the forest made the island one of unwearying changes. Every cloud, every new angle of sun and

The little bay in Coron. This picture is taken from the point
at which Ned Ferguson found the blue orchid.

moon, every squall that passed over it lent new beauty to its rugged features.

"Would you care to visit it?" Hudson asked.

"Can we? I'd like it immensely. But it looks inaccessible."

"There is a place," he said, "where we can climb up without a great deal of difficulty."

We ran along the island for some distance. So far as I could see there was not one place where a man could have scaled the rocky sides which rose straight out of the water to a height of hundreds of feet.

"Here we are."

There was a narrow passage, really only a deep fissure in the rocks but wide enough for our small boat to pass through. We wound around through the stone walls which towered above us on both sides. We traveled possibly fifty yards through a narrow neck and came out into a small bay shut in by forbidding cliffs, except for the opening through which we had come.

I gasped. Hudson shut off the motor and allowed the boat to drift under its own momentum. He sat there watching me and smiling with understanding.

"Hard to believe, isn't it?"

"Yes," I answered. "I would not have supposed that there could be anything so beautiful."

The clear water, smooth and blue as the tropical sky which we could just see above the walls of the canyon, was translucent. On its bottom was a miniature forest of white, black and red coral, and in and out through its colorful branches swam tropical fish like a moving rainbow of blacks and golds and blues and reds.

We drifted under the overhanging branches of a great tree which had managed to take root on the very face of the rock.

"Look up there."

It took me a few seconds to find it—a great white orchid clinging to one of the upper branches.

"This place isn't real," I said. "You should describe heaven ᴬs being like this, Reverend."

"I've something else to show you."

The boat was within ten feet of shore. It was not possible to get it nearer because of the rocks.

"Feel like a little wading?"

"Certainly."

"Then take your shoes off, but bring them along. Wouldn't get far without them on those knife-like rocks over there."

He dropped the boat's small anchor and stepped into the water. I followed.

Reaching the shore, if it could be called that—actually it was only a continuation of the fissure which formed the bay—we found the ascent more gradual. It was hard climbing but he led me up and up—clambering over stones, occasionally finding a small open space.

"Watch your step on the level here," he cautioned. "This erosion extends under the surface. Try each spot before trusting your weight on it. If it should break through there's no telling where you would end up. They tell a story of several men who landed on Coron from an American warship, mysteriously disappearing and never being found. The papers ran the story and I one time met up with a fellow who declared that he was on the ship at the time and that it was true. Maybe so, maybe not. But watch your step. If they did disappear, possibly that's the way they did it."

He had me keeping to the rocks. We had been climbing fifteen or twenty minutes when I straightened up and stared straight ahead. What I saw looked like a huge patch of blue, fallen out of the sky and caught in the rocks of Coron. Again Hudson was grinning.

"That's what I wanted to show you. Isn't it amazing—at this height! It's a lake that has never been fathomed. There are three of these on this island."

We made our way to the edge. We sat on huge boulders and gazed at this startling body of water held in the crown of Coron's summit. There was something terrifying about the mystery of these fathomless indigo waters. A chill passed through me as I looked about at the stony wilderness.

We were halfway back to the boat when I stopped quickly and looked into the branches of a tree which grew on the very edge of the cliff and actually hung over the abyss.

"What is it?" Hudson asked.

"A blue orchid—the smallest I've ever seen." I pointed it out to him. "I must have that."

"Better not. Wouldn't be much left of you if that old tree broke."

"I must have that orchid!"

I climbed the tree and edged out to where I could reach the fragile blossom. Its delicate beauty took my breath.

When I reached the ground, I handed it to Hudson. He turned it about in his hand, looking at it intently.

"I believe this is a new species, Ned. I'm a botanist of sorts, but I've never seen one like this. May I take it to Manila? We may be able to tack your name to it."

I looked far down the rocky ravine to the blue bay where our boat was anchored. Something was stirring deep in me. Beauty, beauty everywhere. Beauty against the background of all that suffering on Culion.

Beauty made possible because of those eroded sides of this mountain in the sea. Erosion which caught the lights and shadows of the day and turned them into a miracle of color.

There came to my mind pictures I had seen of old cathedrals, temples and palaces—beauty rising out of ruins. Why not man? Why must ugliness rise out of the ruins of a man? I had my answer to the problem that had been torturing me.

I would find things to do. I would cheat the empty days. I would make beauty. I would prepare a garden fit for my blue orchid.

I went back to Culion with my mind seething with my new idea. Up to this time I had intended to make my house clean and comfortable and to clear the grounds. Now I began to visualize both as they might be made to be. I walked down to the water's edge and began to sketch. I would plant along the beach a row of tall coconut palms. I would plant them so that between their straight slender trunks I could see the bay and the islands beyond Culion. They would stand like sentinels to guard me against the blazing morning sun and the fury of the typhoon. We had made a beginning at clearing the underbrush; now all of it would go. On my plan I marked a flame tree for a central place on the lawn. I wanted it where its fiery top would greet me the first thing each day. The two fine mango trees now between the house and the sea should remain. I would cover the fence so that it would appear just a hedge of yellow and red hibiscus, and in a corner of the yard I would plant frangipani—waxen blossoms like old ivory, heavy with fragrance. Tomas and I would hunt through the jungles behind the hills for wild orchids. We would plant them in baskets which would hang on the porch. Chief among them would be my blue one. From the edge of the porch would hang the heavy branches of air plants, so avid for life that they grow without soil, clinging to the sides of the trees. Frail, yet hardy, they needed but slight support. A few wires would hold them and their dark green leaves would give an illusion of coolness.

Palms of many varieties must grow in the back country. We two would carry the young plants over the hills and set them outside the bedroom windows. On scorching nights in the dry season their fronds would move and the sound would be that of rain when the earth is parched and thirsty. Up the sides of the house and porch I would train bougainvillaea, brilliant and luxurious in this tropical land, purple and red, and that bronze which they said came from Singapore. Poinsettias, growing fully five feet high, would flame their vivid red-leaf flowers.

The house itself I would turn right around, not literally, but I would make the roadside the back, and here, bordered by flowers, I would have my vegetable garden.

I had arrived this far when Tomas appeared to serve supper. The afternoon had passed without my notice.

"Look, Tomas. I wish you to know what we are going to do to improve our home."

He stood and listened to my enthusiastic description of each tree and bush. I went on and on until I became aware of his growing anxiety as he shifted from one foot to the other. I stopped.

"Yes, sir. I think maybe the beans will be entirely burned, sir." There was tragedy in his boyish face. I roared. Burned beans—when I was building my kingdom as my father before me had built his. Still, Tomas had a kingdom —and in his kingdom beans counted.

"Good gosh! Have the beans been boiling all the time I have been raving?"

"Yes, sir. Even longer."

"Run, Tomas, to the rescue." He was quite cheered up when he found the beans just dry but still unburned. I returned to play, work, illusion; it was as yet all three.

In my turned-about house the living quarters would face the bay and the long lawn would lie between house and beach. It meant completely remodeling the place. I worked far into the night, knocking down partitions, putting in new ones, all on paper and in my imagination. I had an idea I could devise a scheme for making the walls below the windows drop down, so that when the windows were propped up three sides of the room would be almost entirely open. I planned a hall to run from front to back with a bedroom to open off this hall. Tomas would have his room underneath the house proper. He was excited and pleased at the prospect of a domain which would be all his own. A hard clay floor would satisfy his Filipino instinct to sweep down to good clean earth. It would be cooler there than in the house itself. We would engage a lavendera to take the clothes away for washing, so that he would have the whole space, except a small part for storage, to arrange as he willed.

Opening off my bedroom I planned a bathroom—this looked particularly like an illusion but I put it in nevertheless. A little farther along the hall back of the bedroom another door opened into the kitchen.

When I had finished it was very late, but my spirits were high. I was going to have a home that would be an honor to the whole island.

We started work the next morning. Tomas was not exactly enthusiastic about cluttering up the grounds with grass and bushes. Like a true Filipino he would have preferred to scalp a place about the house and keep it neatly swept. However, he was very willing to give all the help he could.

We began clearing. There was considerable debris and the work was slow. The soil was none too good. However, I was determined to get results.

I had a note from Dr. Winton. He had been swamped with work but would be out in a few days. We had been at it over a week when he arrived. Much of the yard brush was cleared down to the soil and it was possible to stand at the house and see beach and sea.

"Man, this is swell!" he exclaimed. "You have been working, haven't you?"

I told him of my plans, but he was not content with that, he wanted to look them over. I watched almost prayerfully.

It was necessary to me that I carry this thing through, and his aid meant much.

"This is great. Why, man, your place will be the show place of the Island. I don't see why you can't do it all. I'll be wanting to swap places with you when you get it done."

The bathroom—I hesitated to ask because I felt certain that would be impossible. But finally I ventured.

"Is there any water near, for the bathroom? Is that at all possible?"

"Sure. I jumped to that when I looked at the plan. You don't mean to tell me you don't know about it? Right along the road a little farther up is a big spring. Tomas probably brings the water you are using from there. You could run pipes down, tapping in above the spring itself; it would not be safe below since the women wash clothing there. Come along, we will go see it."

We found the spring; it was almost a creek, and below it, as Dr. Winton had said, were the lavenderas washing.

"See, there is plenty of water. Now, your lawn worries me. It will dry up, and never come back. But you could tap in again below the spring and use that water for irrigation. There is quite a flow, plenty for all the washing they do, and for your garden."

Robinson Crusoe had nothing on me. In fact I had something on him, a lot of co-operation. But I felt like Crusoe, in my making of a new life, and Tomas was my man Friday. We went at it hard. We had our setbacks. When we began to take down partitions in the house we found timbers ready to fall, eaten by the white ants that are such a pest in these islands. They eat almost anything, utterly destroy the stoutest timbers, leaving nothing but a honeycombed shell, which crumbles to dust at a touch. Luckily they have no taste for nipa. My roof would be safe!

We learned to plait swali; Tomas knew something of that art of palm weaving. I got in some men and women who were experts at it and were glad to teach us. I had difficulty in getting them to accept payment but once it was understood that I could spare the money, they were glad to earn it.

The weeks grew into months, with little variation. Our living was reduced to a simple routine; my orders from Manila came regularly. Tomas, as Winton had predicted, was an excellent house boy. He had learned to cook, too, helped by the women about, and my own knowledge, especially in the preparation of American dishes. In fact he was always springing something new on me. Gradually our meals became a mixture of American and Filipino food. I secured a lavendera to wash our clothes. Much of this was made possible because Dr. Winton had succeeded in getting my pension. I wrote Tom that I would need no more money. (Our letters were disinfected, of course, before they left the Island.) At Christmas, nevertheless, Tom sent me two hundred dollars. I ordered some new furniture and the bathroom fixtures. We put a sink in the kitchen and a shower in the bath. We built our own septic tank. We never had to heat water for a bath, the temperature took care of that.

The yard was slower work. Still, at the end of my first year we had done a great deal. Tomas and I had spent days in the wilderness back of us, carrying home small trees and plants. We dug up soil and carried it from the interior two buckets at a time, slung across poles over our backs. It was slow work but I had all time. We got fertilizers from Manila with seeds of grasses suited to our climate. A carpet of green was beginning to appear at the edge of the porch and stretch down to the shadows of the coconut palms. They were small shadows as yet, but the trees were healthy and well rooted. The hibiscus was all planted and the bougainvillaea was climbing up the sides of the porch. My flame tree was in, and I nursed it with the care of a fond parent. The air plants had already grown to the point of shielding me from the morning sun when I ate breakfast on my porch room.

The two stately mango trees, cleared of undergrowth, now framed a splendid view of the bay from the house. They were my chief pride. In their shadow stood some wooden chairs, which we had painted white. After they had been finished, Dr. Winton sent someone to spray them. When visitors came they took certain of the chairs reserved for them. Tomas and I never touched those chairs and we warned any of the colonists who were calling not to use them.

Down on the beach I had placed some benches, and in the evening after supper I would sit and watch the stars. I liked to watch the moon climb slowly above the crest of Coron. The moonlight streamed over the reefs like molten silver. I was living in a new world, learning it slowly, almost as primitive man must have learned it, night and day, night and day. And the months wore on, and on.

CHAPTER ✓ ✓ ✓ ✓ ✓ ✓ ✓ ✓ ✓ ✓ ✓ FIFTEEN

Iᴛ ᴡᴀs ᴀʟᴍᴏsᴛ ᴛᴡᴏ ʏᴇᴀʀs sɪɴᴄᴇ ᴍʏ ᴀʀʀɪᴠᴀʟ
at Culion when Tom wrote me that mother had died.
She had never been a strong woman, and the past year she
had just weakened bit by bit. She was not old, not yet sixty.
It was impossible for me to imagine home without
mother. . . .

"I'm sending you," wrote Tom, "the blue dishes mother
kept just for the family, which you always liked so much."

Those dishes took me back into my world of the past.
Mother had received them as a wedding gift. I remembered
them clearly because their infrequent use had marked some
very special family occasion, such as the wedding anniver-
sary of my parents, or a birthday. They were English china,
gold edged and blue bordered, with white centers containing a spray of red and blue flowers. Nothing Tom could
have sent me would have pleased me as much. I hoped that
they would come through the long journey intact.

Then I went back to the letter.

Business had been very bad, but there was much talk that the war in Europe would mean a boom in America. It was the end of the letter that troubled me most.

"Some people say we won't be able to keep out, if there is a war. Well, if there is one I am going in."

That hit me hard. I fell to thinking of our family: a man in every war since the Revolution. I was no pacifist, but somehow I did wish Tom could stay out. War. . . . I fell to thinking of my wounds. My leprosy was a war product; anyhow, Tom would not get that in Europe.

From the first week of my arrival I had been taking treatments regularly. Winton had explained that the patients were divided into groups, each reporting to his clinic once a week. Men and women attended different clinics. The Director of Health had introduced a new treatment, but its use was optional. The new way was the giving of chaulmoogra oil by injections. It did not have the bad effects that so often followed the taking of the oil by mouth. Many of the patients feared injections, and were allowed to continue the old form of treatment. I elected the new method.

When I went to my first appointment I found a number of men standing about the door or crowded into the small wooden building which served as one of the clinics. Waiting our turns, we became well acquainted. We talked of the colony and the colonists, and then passed to more impersonal subjects. They were curious, but entirely polite, in their interest in the United States, and when I was moved to hold forth I always had a most attentive audience.

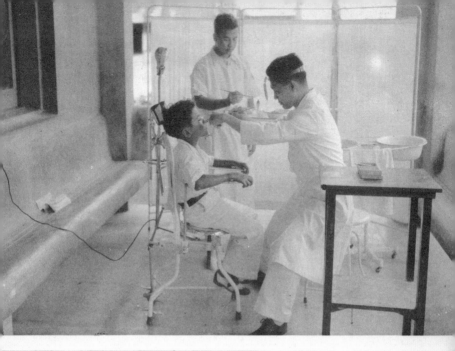

(top) Tomas receiving treatment at the clinic.

(bottom) One of the modern hospitals at Culion.

The back country of the island of Culion.

The leper cemetery at Culion looking toward Church Hill.

A typical street in the colony.

The officiating physician, Dr. Crisolgo, was one of Winton's assistants. Helping him was a trained nurse. Against the walls of the little room were a few wooden chairs and a couple of wooden tables. The nurse sat at one of these with a card file before her. The cards held the name and record of each patient and when I came in mine was lying on the table. Both doctor and nurse greeted me pleasantly by name. Dr. Crisolgo, who was disinfecting his hands in a bowl, asked me several questions about my present state of health.

"I understand, Mr. Ferguson, that you are very actively engaged in remodeling your house and grounds. I trust that I may be permitted to call upon you some day to see what you have done. Dr. Winton is most enthusiastic."

"You will be welcome," I responded.

Then I was asked to give a detailed account of my previous treatment, that is, before coming to Culion, and a record was made of my report.

"Is Tuesday at this time convenient for you to come for treatment, Mr. Ferguson?" the nurse asked.

And me with all the time there was! I never saw people more considerate. They were rushed with more patients than the size of the staff warranted, yet I was consulted as to my choice of a day and hour for treatment.

"It is entirely convenient," I assured her.

Dr. Crisolgo explained that the injections were given intramuscularly.

"There are a number of patients who take no treatment at all, I am sorry to say. We do not, as yet, insist upon it. But you are wise, Mr. Ferguson, and I hope you will be faithful in continuing. It is true that the treatment is too new to know what the results will be. But we are all hopeful."

"I'll be here regularly," I promised.

My own reaction was slight. No one likes to be punctured with a needle, but I felt little discomfort after it was over. Sometimes immediately following the treatment a man would be seized with a violent coughing spell or he would be dizzy. Luckily I escaped both. As often as I went, I seemed never to tire of watching the others, and this was true of most patients.

I liked to study their faces, trying to guess what they were thinking as they winced under the thrust of the needle. Was it simple resignation? Or—was it hope? Did they dream as they endured their discomfort of a time when they would return home?

As our work grew less and less, Tomas and I shortened our working day. I was at the point where I understood that first chapter of Genesis. I could look upon my work and find it good. So could Tomas. It had taken some persuasion on my part to make him believe that the place was his as well as mine. But at last he accepted the idea. He now took great pride in his home and would invite his friends to call and show them about.

Tomas had developed rapidly during the two years he had spent at Culion. Although at the clinic he still gave a positive reaction to tests, there was no indication that the disease was advancing. There was one hardly discernible patch on his face and there were two others on his hips. Except for these and the laboratory report he seemed a healthy, fine-looking lad. The work was good for him. He was now capable of running the house with very little assistance from me.

One especially hot day at the end of the dry season I was lounging on the porch waiting for Tomas to return with the mail. The little inter-island steamer had sounded her whistle some time before. I heard the gate open and I looked up expectantly toward the corner of the house. It was not Tomas. Instead, a tall, bearded stranger, obviously American, came to the steps and stood there, staring at me.

"You don't know me, do you, Ned?" I knew the voice. But while I was digging into the past for his name, he went on.

"I'm Bob—Bob Sellars."

"Bob Sellars! Where in the name of Heaven did you come from? You—you were not sent down here, were you?"

"No, not that. I just came down to see you."

"Bob, that was damned decent of you. Come along. I have some special chairs for visitors, out under the mangoes."

"I'm not afraid. I envy you all this." I started. Bob had grown to be a big man, taller and heavier than I was, and I tipped the scales at one hundred and eighty-five pounds. He looked well, but his clothes were shabby.

"You—envy me? You know I am a leper."

"Yeah, I know. I'm a kind of leper myself. I'm a man without a country, and what is worse, a man without a people. I sound crazy, don't I? Guess I am crazy, or near crazy at that. When I was with the constabulary, I met a girl, a native. She was a beauty and I fell in love with her. We married. My wife is a fine woman, Ned. When I finished my term of enlistment I started a little business, a restaurant, in Iloilo but could not make a go of it. Her folks are high class Filipinos, but they've no use for me. I can't seem to make any money. We have five children. I love my wife and I think she still loves me. But—well, you know how Filipinos are about their families. It's breaking her, Ned; it's breaking her. Sometimes I think she'd be better off if I cut and went home. But there are the children; they are mine, you know. I go clear off thinking about it all."

Bob stayed three days. Winton arranged a place for him in Balala. He would come up bright and early every morning. He brought his lunch in a bag, and we would discuss old times.

That first day he was not the Bob I had known. His spirit seemed completely broken. He looked worried, and there was deep suffering in his eyes.

"Ned, how did you keep going when you found out about things?"

"Bill Thompson and my brother kept me from suicide. They believed in me; I couldn't let them down."

I told him how Bill had pointed out that I could take it lying down or on my feet.

"You had grit."

"So have you," I told him. His eyes brightened. "You really think so, Ned?"

He did not mention the subject the rest of the day. He talked much less than he had previously.

The next morning he seemed a changed man. His step had quickened.

"Ned, I'm going to make a fresh start. There's a miniature gold rush up in the Benguet region. Maybe I can get in, and later take my wife and children there. It's beautiful country; she would like it. Particularly if I were making good."

"Bob, you'll need money for a start. Let me help you. I have a small income and very little need of it down here."

"I can't take your money."

"Of course you can. It will mean a lot to me."

"Well, if you put it that way, all right. I need very little and will return it to you just as soon as I can. Ned, you've saved my life."

"Nonsense," I replied.

The next day he left.

A well man had come over two hundred miles to consult me, a leper. The thought of that was tonic to my morale.

ONE DAY, AFTER BOB'S VISIT AND BEFORE the rains had set in, Dr. Winton came to see me. We strolled out onto the lawn.

I had a swimming beach for myself and Tomas, cleared of sharp stones and nettles, but it was not always safe, for sharks occasionally came in. We had rigged a kind of screen to keep them out but high seas frequently swept this away and it had to be replaced. This day heat lay on the Island like a blanket. I could see Tomas's head bobbing about on the water. The inner bay was untouched by the faintest breeze, the water lay limpid against the shore. The shrill din of the cicadas rose from the bougainvillaea almost drowning our voices, rose in unbroken and sharpening crescendo, our nerves tautening with the rise until they were ready to snap, and then there would be sudden silence as oppressive as the noise. That would be broken by the harsh call of a gecko and then the cicadas would start again.

"Devilish things these cicadas," said Winton, lifting his glass of tansan. I had managed to obey the rules and still dispense a kind of hospitality by keeping soft drinks in the shed. Guests had to help themselves. They brought their own cups.

"Yes, they are," I admitted. "But, there's something more devilish. It's these idle hours. You know as well as I do that while I am not much worse than when I came, I am not better."

"Yes, I know, but you must not give up hope, Ned. We all believe the injections are going to work wonders."

"The trouble with this, Winton, is that it is a waiting game and I've been playing it a long, long time. I've finished my house and now I have nothing to do. I am terrified at facing idleness. If I have to sit here from morning to night and contemplate my own disintegration—well, I can't do it."

I stopped. I was making articulate for the first time the thoughts that had haunted me for months. I was amazed at my own earnestness, almost vehemence.

"I understand, but it's not easy to furnish employment in a place like this."

"But it shouldn't be so. Work should be found for them."

"But, you can't go into people's homes and arrest father or son because he is a leper, bring him down here and force him to work, now can you? Then, of course, some of these people are not able to work."

"Maybe you can't. But as a physician do you believe that they, your patients, I mean, would be injured or benefited by a reasonable amount of work?"

"You know the answer to that, Ned. If a patient is happy in what he is doing, he benefits, provided he is kept from overtaxing his strength."

"Well, there are more than thirty-five hundred people here now. Many of them will never see their homes again. They must find life right here."

"There is employment for some. There are the stores—we employ a few as teachers. But you are right. We do not have any organized work."

"Take this place of mine, Winton. I used a good many men first and last. I talked with them and they all wanted something to do, or at least said they did. I admit that what I could give them was not steady work and they earned only a little."

"That's just it. There is occasional work like yours. What can you give these people to do continuously, year in and year out? I'd like you to name one thing."

"All right. You have a contract with a company from the outside to supply fish. The fish are right here. Many of your patients have been fishermen, a lot more could learn. Why don't you give them a chance?"

"Well, for one thing it's impossible. You don't realize the quantity of fish needed to feed almost four thousand people. The colonists here do not have sufficient equipment. They could not be depended upon, if they had. They just couldn't do it."

"It's true that there are many who could not be depended upon. Whenever you give people all their necessities there will be many who will just sit in the sun all day. That's true anywhere—not just here. But, as I've said, there are also a lot of these people who want to work. Of course the thing must be organized if it is to be successful. But it can be done. Even some of those who at present prefer just to loaf will get other ideas if it is made sufficiently attractive. I'll admit they couldn't supply four thousand people with fish tomorrow. But they could supply a part. You bring these men here and condemn them to idleness. It speaks well for them that they have made this place as good to look at as it is. God knows they have little incentive. The shops speak well for them; the fact that their women pound clothes until they are white speaks well for them. But all outside markets are closed. Then you close their own market, and turn it over to well people. I think it's rotten."

He took it, twisting the bowl of his pipe in his fist.

"What do you want?"

It took my breath. What did I want? But I knew, although I had never said it aloud.

"I want a contract for fresh fish up to a certain amount. Pay what you pay the outsiders. I'll get the men together; I know there are men here eager to work."

"We'll be running against prejudice if we tackle it. There are a good many people who would feel that lepers should not do any work. Then as Medical Director I'd have to take the responsibility for certifying the men able to work without impairing their strength."

"You'll find Father Marello and Mr. Hudson supporting the idea," I said, smiling. "I talked with them when the men worked on the house. Not about this idea; I didn't have it then, but just about the general idea of work."

"Possibly—but suppose I give you such a contract and you employ one of the patients and he has a bad reaction?

I'd be in a fix. We Americans have to watch our step in these islands. There are politicians aplenty who wouldn't come within a hundred miles of this place, but who know just what ought to be done. And your part. As manager you would receive a salary. And you would just be a smart American exploiting your fellows. I'd like to see it tried but I just can't see how it could be worked."

"The money is simple. I've got my pension and the house. My expenses are light. Give me nothing. That will silence your politicians if they fuss. We'll organize a mutual profit company among the men. I'll take my chance with the others; the money is not the important thing with me." He sat mulling it over. A breeze was starting and the branches of the palms moved lazily. The shrilling chorus of the cicadas died away.

"Sign that the rains will start soon, so they say." Winton rose, knocked the ashes out of his pipe by hitting it against the heel of his left hand, and started for the gate. There he stopped and looked at me hard. "I'm going to think about your fishing party, Ned. Good night."

I watched him down the road. I had got past the doctor in him anyhow. He was considering the problem from a man's standpoint.

Reverend Hudson had been down several weeks and was shortly to return to Manila on a boat which was arriving with patients from Cebu on the fifth. He dropped in a few days beforehand to say good-by.

At the edge of the house we came upon Tomas squatting with a huge, flaming rooster between his hands. He was smoothing its feathers with a rhythmic stroke and crooning to it as a mother croons to her child.

"What a beauty, Tomas! Where did you get him?"

"Mr. Ferguson gave him to me, sir, for my birthday. He is all time being very much kind to me."

I felt a little fussed. Tomas had from the first done more for me than I could ever hope to repay. Birthdays were mournful occasions for Tomas. I had tried to make him forget by buying this fine fighting cock from one of our neighbors, Hilario La Rosa. It saved the day. I had tethered it in his room at dawn. When Tomas, aroused by its indignant fussing, understood that the bird was his, I think he forgot home, including mother and baby sister. No rooster could hope to accomplish more. Every free moment since had been spent in exercising, feeding, and just staying with his prize.

"Going to fight him?" asked Reverend Hudson.

"Oh, but yes, sir. I should not be so very unkind to him as not to let him fight. He will fight in the colony pit on the day of the Independence of the United States of America."

The day of Independence was being honored, there was no doubt as to that.

"You mean the Fourth of July, Tomas. I notice you Filipinos make about as much fuss on that day as on Rizal Day. How can you explain that?"

"Oh, sir, that is because Uncle Sam is a very big and powerful gentleman. He all the time was looking for independence just the same as Mr. Rizal and all Filipino peoples. He come to the Philippines with many big battleships and he sink the Spanish ships. He say to Filipino people, 'Now, I teach you how to be independent. I teach you English language and how to be good American citizens and by and by you learn to be independent.' On Fourth of July American people make much noise and the cannon go off, and are most happy thinking of the Boston tea party. Pretty soon maybe Filipinos have tea party and be happy— so Filipinos make much noise on Fourth of July."

"Well, Tomas, good luck to you and your bird."

"Thank you, sir. He will win."

Hudson turned to me. "I wonder, Ned, whether we haven't got it all in a nutshell right there. We must not for-

Tomas with his fighting cock, Mystery.

get in our dealing with the Filipinos that all people, everywhere, want to have their own tea party. The hunger for freedom is universal and deep. We must deal with these people patiently and understandingly. Some day they will be given their independence. We have promised it to them when they are ready. We must make certain that we have not left them unprepared when that day comes. We can't do that unless we work with them sympathetically. In my own case, for instance. As a churchman, I feel that we who come out to these places as representatives of the churches must keep an open mind and an understanding spirit toward the people whom we wish to serve. Personally I do not approve of cockfights, but that should not prevent my understanding Tomas's natural passion for it, heritage of the centuries. If I permitted it to blind me to the fine sentiment to which he has just given utterance I would be a fool."

I respected Hudson. He was a man of great understanding.

July second, and already the streets of the colony were gay with American and Philippine flags, and red, white and blue bunting. Winton had sent for me, and as I walked to the Colony Hall I, as an American, was greeted from all sides.

"Good morning, Mr. Ferguson. Do you see the colony makes preparation for the Fourth of July?"

"How do you do, Mr. Ferguson? Soon it will be Independence Day. Is your flagpole finished, sir?"

"Not quite—but it will be by the Fourth." I was erecting a tall pole between the mangoes and the beach. At Win ton's office I talked with patients in the anteroom. Unobtrusively, I looked them over to see how many appeared fit for labor. A few were obviously unfit. There were those with the characteristic claw fingers of the nerve type of leprosy, and those whose hands and feet were heavily bandaged. But there were others who were certainly strong and capable. I had lost consciousness of racial differences. I had become accustomed to the smaller size of the Filipino and I was about as brown as he. The tan I had acquired was no tan at all, but a deep brown that never left me.

Finally Winton was ready for me. As I came in he was reading a slip of paper. "News for you, Ned. All kinds of news! Sancho's sister is arriving with the patients who are coming down on this boat."

"Huh, maybe," I retorted. Half a dozen times before I had heard that Carita was on her way. But for one reason or another she had not appeared.

"She is really coming this time, old man. Seems to be quite a person. Teaches dancing, supervises games and recreational activities. It appears that while the family is not well off, they are fine people. The mother is Spanish. You probably know all about this—"

"Yes, I knew the family and I've kept in touch with them through Bob Sellars."

"And now," went on Winton, "for more news. The Director of Health, Dr. Marshall, is coming on the same boat. He has resigned, and is leaving the Philippines this month. This is to be his last visit. He insisted on making the final trip and gathering up all the patients he could. He wants to see you; he can stay only a few hours before he returns to Manila.

"And—one of our clerks who has been to Manila is bringing you something special, a message from your brother."

My heart missed a beat.

"There's nothing wrong with Tom, is there? He hasn't got—leprosy?"

"No, no, Ned. I'm sorry I upset you. It's just a special gift that he has sent."

What a relief!

"And still more news. We are just full of news today. I am going to make a try at your plan; at least I am going to give you a chance to have a go at it. We can help you to this extent. We can buy your fish—if you can get them. There are certain contracts already in force, as you know. But with the steady growth of the colony, we will need more. We will figure on a definite number of kilos, if you can get them and see that they are fresh. Remember, you will have to find some way to guarantee a constant supply. Now work it out, then come back and we will talk over the details of an agreement between us."

I left with my mind seething with this new and exciting problem. Plaza Libertad was festive. I climbed the long stone steps to see whether any of the men I had thought of coming in with me were about. Not a one was there, of course, although the square was full as usual. I hung around an hour or so, hearing much about the coming celebration and about the cockfight.

"I hear Tomas has fine rooster."

"You know name we give him? We call him Mystery bird."

"Will you bet many pesos on him when he fights, Mr. Ferguson?"

They all laughed. One boy said: "Poor Pedro Gomez! Five times he have championship cock. And now I think after Independence Day he have big stew!"

A fellow sitting beside him spoke up: "For how many pesos do you think?" I turned to him.

"Five pesos, Julian, if you wish."

They all laughed until Julian dug down into his pocket and covered the bet.

There were a number who were placing small bets on Tomas's bird. It had not yet fought, but its very appearance had been enough to encourage speculation. Filipinos are inveterate gamblers and the talk waxed warm. In the middle of it José Cruz arrived and I slipped away with him and began to talk about the great plan. José lived not far from me, and had helped on the house.

"Do you mean to say, Mr. Ferguson, that we could make money—all the time?" he asked incredulously.

"That's the idea, José. Of course it may not work out."

"I'd do almost anything to make money," he said slowly. "I know that I am sick, but yet I am not so terribly sick, and this having nothing to do is, I think, most bad for those of us who can work. I should like to work for myself as long as I am able. Before I came here, I had sometimes assisted in the building of boats, but I cannot claim to be a fisherman. If you will take me, I will do my very best."

"Good. Come along to my place tomorrow. You might bring Manuel Zanilla. I will get some of the other men and we will talk about it."

Manuel Zanilla was the first man who had spoken to me

when I awoke in San Lazaro, with Tomas snuggling against me. He had been delayed in getting to Culion but had been there several months.

José was the first to arrive the following afternoon. He was bubbling over with enthusiasm. "This is truly an important day, Mr. Ferguson. Very much I have needed occupation."

Manuel came in a state of equal excitement. "It is of significance that tomorrow is Independence Day. Here we begin an independence of our own."

Federico Arang was no stranger to my house. For almost two years he had been acting as tutor to Tomas, and he was always a welcome visitor. Three years before he had been taken from all that life held for him. He was a lawyer, and had been graduated from the University of San Tomas, founded in 1611 and therefore the oldest university in any territory under the American flag. He had just passed his bar examinations when it was discovered that he had lesions. He was sent at once to San Lazaro and afterwards to Culion.

When I met him he was the President of the Leper Council, which was the elected body representing the patients. The council advised with the administration upon matters pertaining to the general welfare, and also controlled certain affairs concerning individual rights and responsibilities. Never have I met so unhappy a man. His profession had been snatched away from him after he had labored for years to secure his education. When he first came he was known as "the silent one." He would walk through the colony, head down, seeing no one. He rarely spoke. The hut which he chose for his home he occupied alone, and he had fixed it up nicely. He did his own work, even his cooking. The colony gossip had it that he was profoundly attached to his wife and his two young children from whom he had been taken so suddenly. When I approached him to ask him to tutor Tomas he accepted at once, and sent every cent home to his family.

This afternoon he had come at my earnest request. He had entered with indifference which soon vanished. The truth was that he was a good organizer and even at that first meeting he whipped my simple little plan into A-1 shape. Every man there clearly understood what our work was to be, and what was more important, our relationship, in that work, to each other.

After Arang's able explanation they understood fully what they were to do, and they joined up readily, assuring me that they could get as many men as were needed. In my two years on the Island it was the first time I had seen men excited about anything in their own interest. Celebrations and fiestas were in honor of heroes or of country. Here was a new kind of excitement—for lepers; the possibility of achievement and of a chance to make money for themselves and their families. Tomas served us cake and chilled milk of the coconuts. They were very enthusiastic about the whole scheme when they left. Even Arang's head was lifted, and as for Manuel, he sang "The Star-spangled Banner" all the way down the road.

After they had gone I put the whole plan together, working it out on my typewriter preparatory to taking it first to Arang, for approval, and then to Winton. That night I came down with an attack of dengue fever and everything was off. I missed the Fourth of July celebration. Dengue fever is mean. My temperature ran to 104. My head and eyes and joints and muscles ached. Winton dropped in and looked at me.

"You stop all planning and just rest," he ordered.

"I've heard the Negroes at home talk about 'breakbone fever,'" I groaned, "but I never knew what suffering it meant."

"That will pass in a day or so. And don't be alarmed if you begin to break out in eruptions. It's all a part of the course of the fever."

That was enough to send my spirits to a new low. Tomas was torn between his loyalty to me and his obligations to the cockpit. I urged him to go, pointing out that I had an interest in Mystery, as we now called the bird, and I handed him five more pesos to wager. With his leaving time ceased. I was wandering miserably through a land of hallucination in which I was assaulted by savages pricking me all over with barbed points, when through the agony I heard the boy's voice.

"Mr. Ferguson! Mr. Ferguson! Oh, sir, we have won! We have won!"

Tomas had returned, the bird under his arm, the boy almost beside himself.

"He fought the champion of the colony. Many lost plenty of pesos. But we did not lose any. Here are yours, sir, and I have won much more."

I sat up. My head roared, but this was decidedly better than being stuck with barbs, even if the barbs were but imaginary.

"Where did you get money to bet, Tomas?"

"Oh, I all time save the pesos you give me, sir. I bet them all because I know good fighting cock, and I am very certain we win."

"And now what will you do with so much, Tomas?"

"It is that about which I wish to speak with you. But you are sick, maybe I make too much trouble."

"I'm glad to have someone to talk with. Go ahead, Tomas."

"I wish very much that you would ask the Chief of the Colony to be so kind as to send thirty pesos to my mother, and ask her if when it is Visitors' Day she will come to see me. I feel sure that she will not wish to come unless she has a new dress. This will be enough for her to come to Manila and to buy a dress of a nice kind. I shall keep five pesos, because on Rizal Day there will be a very big fight. Dr. Crisolgo at the fight today had with him a guest. This man said he has a very fine fighter and will bring him to fight on that day. We shall then win again, and it is for that I wish to keep the five pesos."

"Tomas, that is dandy. When your mother comes, you must bring her here. I shall want to meet her, you know." Tears came into his eyes as he thanked me.

With that he left the room and as he passed into the hall I caught a glimpse of him. He suddenly pulled the rooster up against his cheek.

"Thank you very much, too," I heard him whisper.

THE GOVERNMENT BOAT WITH THE PATIENTS arrived on the fifth. I could not go to meet it. Father Marello stopped in, and promised he would explain to Carita and bring her to visit me as soon as I could see her. My illness had put clear out of my mind the gift which was coming from Tom. I was delighted when I found that it was a high-powered rifle. Because of the law restricting the bringing of firearms into the Islands, the clerk had seen to the necessary formalities and had personally brought it down. No kid with his first air rifle brought by Santa Claus had anything on me.

When Dr. Marshall came to call I was sitting up in bed playing with the gun. After a warm exchange of greetings, he remarked, "That's a fine piece. Heavy enough for tamarau." My heart leaped.

"Do you really think so? I'd like to try for one, just once."

161

We talked about the war which had been raging for a year in Europe. He thought there was no possibility of the United States being drawn in. President Wilson was committed to a policy of neutrality.

"An improved form of the chaulmoogra treatment is coming, Ferguson," he said as he left. "When we meet again, you'll be back home, and a well man." I believed him —for a minute. When his footsteps passed down the walk, I reverted at once. I knew that others were improving; I saw them. I was not. Still, the treatment might have checked advance, for I was not a great deal worse than when I arrived.

After he had gone I lay there thinking about this man, Winton and the others. What impressed me most was their friendship, not only with me but with all lepers. They and their colleagues had waged war on disease with success. The great plagues, cholera, smallpox, malaria, had been checked and greatly diminished. The death rate in the Philippines had been appalling; it was much less.* Probably few people in the United States would ever realize how much had been done.

Ten days after the boat left I was on my feet. The Padre and Mr. Hudson had been in and out a number of times. Father Marello reported Carita concerned for my illness. She was in one of the dormitories and was looking very well.

"This thing is about over, Father. Do you think it would be all right to ask Carita to come for tea?"

* 1905 deaths from all causes per 1,000 pop., 27.5; 1913, 18.8.

"I think it would cheer you up, Ned. I'll convey your invitation to her. Shall we say tomorrow afternoon?"

This was my first party in over three years. I was so excited that I routed Tomas out extra early the next morning and how we did work! That tea was to be a "high tea." We were both fair cooks by this time but I got ambitious and tried out a recipe for small iced cakes. The net result was that at noon Tomas and I were worn out; there were three batches of dismal failures sitting around an untidy kitchen —and no edible cakes. I had not confided the name of my visitor to Tomas as I feared his excitement might impair his abilities. Looking at the last sodden batch we had taken from the oven he said mournfully:

"I think, sir, very big man come to see you. Maybe Governor-General. Is it not so that you make so very much mess?" This mild rebuke convinced me that my loyal Tomas had reached the breaking point. I did not wonder— I was there myself.

"Look, Tomas, it is not the Governor-General but a lady, an old friend. Now take these pesos and go down to the tiendas and hunt about for the nicest cakes you can find. Little cakes, pretty ones with icing all over them. Sugar— you know the kind."

"Oh, yes, sir. The lady will like them much. It is much better, sir." And he was off.

I was wholly unprepared for the vision of loveliness that came through my gate at five that afternoon. The Padre was with her but I hardly saw him. Carita had been a pretty child. When I was with the Nolascos she might have been sixteen, plump, shy, a bit roguish, and very intelligent, as I found out when I was teaching her English. Thirteen years later she was a rather tall, slim, gracious lady of extreme beauty. Her skin was the color of old ivory and the texture extremely fine—her mother had been pure Spanish. There was no mark of the disease. Her hair, ebony, was smoothed back from her high brow and lay in heavy coils low on her neck. She wore one of the exquisite mestizo dresses of pine-apple cloth, an odd rose color embroidered in silver. The large, transparent, starched sleeves were completed by a fichu worn about the shoulders. She carried the train of her skirt daintily in one hand.

After the first shock I began to be uncomfortable. I wondered whether my tie was all right. There was little time for thought. I spoke hastily to Father Marello, who had accompanied her. Then I saw that she was holding out a small delicately formed hand. That gave me a thrill—I shook hands very seldom.

"I am most sorry you are here, Ned—but it is nice to see you again."

She had the poise common to educated Filipino ladies. I was more awkward in my reply.

"I was deeply shocked when I knew about you, Carita. And Sancho—"

"Poor Sancho. It is well that he is no longer here."

We were silent for a moment. Then she recovered and began to smile.

"Father Marello has told me about the wonders of your house and garden. For that matter, everyone I meet tells me of them."

"You are very kind to say that. Won't you come around

the house? The most comfortable place is under the mango trees."

When we were seated Father Marello spoke up with a twinkle in his eye.

"Ned, you never told me how pretty she is."

Carita protested.

"Father, I do not think it a good example for a priest of the Church to exaggerate—" How wonderful her great eyes were!

"No, I didn't, Father, because Carita—well, she wasn't a beautiful woman, then. Just a nice little girl. As for a priest —I believe in beauty, wherever it is found; I hold with the Padre."

She laughed. After a time we three strolled around the grounds. I did little talking. The Padre pointed out the flame tree and some of the rarer orchids. She was especially interested in the blue one and made me promise to tell her some day of my finding it. When we paused at the front and looked down toward the bay with its row of tall coconut trees, she stood entranced.

"Ned, this is lovely. I think I have never seen a more wonderful frame for a beautiful picture."

"Well, I am leaving you two," Father Marello declared finally. "I have to get to the hospital. Carita, you will hardly know your way back. Ned, are you well enough to see Carita to the dormitory?"

"I feel great," I assured him.

"I haven't told Carita about the fishing venture. I left that for you."

When he had gone and Tomas was setting the blue

dishes on a table placed under the trees, Carita turned to me.

"What did he mean by the fishing venture?"

I told her what I intended to do, and how the dengue had temporarily stopped operations.

"You have begun something that will meet a great need," she said thoughtfully. "I started to teach dancing at Cebu for much the same reason, but work is better than play, for all of us. When I was first sent to Cebu I thought I would lose my mind. I was very ill for months. I could not eat. I just desired to slip from life. One of the Sisters of my Church would not leave me. Little by little she roused me from my inertia. She won my affection. And then, with her, I began working with the young girls. They had the courage I lacked."

Shyly Tomas came with the tea. Carita welcomed him.

"Tomas, I have heard of your wonderful cock. You must show him to me. I understand you became very rich on July Fourth and that you will be still richer after Rizal Day?"

Tomas was grinning from ear to ear.

"You hear rightly, Señora. When you and Mr. Ferguson finish your tea, please will you visit me? I will with gladness show you the cock. You know that Mr. Ferguson gave him to me and that he is always so kind—"

"We'll be back to see Mystery," I interrupted.

The tea and the capital iced cakes Tomas had secured were disposed of. We visited the cock, and Carita, whose knowledge of fighting birds seemed prodigious, prophesied a winning on Rizal Day.

"It really is a most remarkable bird," she said as we

strolled down to the bay. I felt suddenly that I was quite well. I had watched, entranced, while Carita poured the tea. Her graciousness invested the simple service with a quality foreign to my daily life. We sat there on the beach and talked of "ships and shoes and sealing wax"—that is, of leper colonies, of old days in Luzon, of Carita's father and mother and brothers and sisters.

The glow of the setting sun faded from the sides of Coron; the shadows lengthened across the bay until they touched the shores on the other side. Still we talked and joked and laughed—it was like being re-born.

Carita started to her feet. "I must go. You have made the hours so delightful I had forgotten. Those of my household will be disturbed about my supper—not that I can eat more. But they are so good they will be keeping it hot for me."

We started on our way back to the road and down it. I was happier than I had been for years.

CHAPTER ′ ′ ′ ′ ′ ′ ′ ′ ′ ′ NINETEEN

I HAD NEVER ASSOCIATED WITH ANY OF THE
women on the Island, but now it seemed natural that fiestas
should be attended by Carita and me together. At first with
great ceremony and then with no ceremony at all she became a visitor at my house, and it was taken for granted
that she would stay for tea, or supper. She was there when
Tomas, his great eyes shining, brought his mother to meet
me. Mrs. Aguilar was a worn and faded woman who must
have been pretty when she was a girl. Her features were
those of her son. She seemed bewildered and ill at ease.
What she had expected to find I could only imagine.

With her usual tact, Carita managed to make the visit a
very pleasant one. In this, Mystery was a great aid. Tomas
had brought his mother direct to me, so that she had not
seen the bird which had made her visit possible. Tomas
brought the rooster for her to admire.

"When he fight on Rizal Day, I shall send you many

pesos. You will see." He was a good prophet; within a few months Mystery had won another fight and was looked upon as the champion.

We left them chatting happily, almost gaily. At the end of the day when she came to say good-by, Tomas's mother quite broke down. Weeping, she tried to thank me for what she called the boy's start in life. Carita took her to the beach and they had a long talk. When Mrs. Aguilar left us, she was apparently contented.

"The poor woman was completely upset," said Carita. "She is very happy now, I think. At least one of her children is provided for. You have been good to Tomas, Ned."

"He earns his way. I don't give him anything he doesn't deserve. Come, Carita, I have some new records. Let's dance." We often danced in the evenings and had endless talks about the men, the business and the work Carita was doing.

That night we walked along the beach. A full moon was over Coron, silvering the tops of the coconut palms, throwing patterns of black shadows across the glittering sands. We stood there drinking in the beauty of the night. I looked at her, exquisite in her lovely native gown. I was trying to get up my courage to speak. I took her hand. She made no move to withdraw it. Suddenly there came a long, loud howl from upshore and at once there was a chorus of them, savage and mournful, that turned blood to ice. With a frightened cry Carita slipped into my arms and I soothed her with little broken speeches.

"Don't, Carita. It's only the wild dogs in the cemetery."

"In the cemetery!"

She shivered. I bent over and kissed her again and again. I held her closer. We forgot our peril, forgot our doom, forgot everything except that the night was ours. I carried her back into the house. It was dawn when I walked down the road with her.

"Don't come any farther, Ned."

"You—you will be all right?"

"I'll go to the Romeros' house. I shall not return to the dormitory. Getulio Romero is my father's cousin. They will not question. Good night, my darling."

She walked down the road.

Two weeks passed. I had not seen Carita in all that time, and I was almost crazy. I met Getulio in the Plaza and stopped him.

"I haven't seen Carita for days."

"She is not well, Ned."

I went home and tried to think it through. Had Getulio been telling me the truth? Was Carita evading me or was she really ill? There was one possible explanation I rejected again and again but it would return. Could it be that she was going to have a baby?

I wanted Carita. She loved me. There was no reason in the world why we should not marry.

A kind of fierce joy ran through me. Fate was to be cheated and I was to have my happiness after all. But, if there was to be a baby! Would it be a leper, too?

I thought of what Winton had told me, that there were over a hundred children born to patients every year. That they were not born lepers, that leprosy was not inherited, but that they were so susceptible to infection that as soon as possible they were taken from their mothers and transferred to the nursery just outside the colony proper. Eventually they were sent away and unless they contracted leprosy or their parents were cured—they would never see them again. While the children remained on the Island mothers might visit them but not touch them. Now, torn by this idea, I went down to this nursery. There were more than twenty mothers waiting in the little pavilion. Above and opposite them was the long balcony of the nursery.

A Sister in white came out on the balcony carrying an infant. There was a long drawn "A-ah!" and one of the women, almost a girl, pressed forward, holding up her hands. It was hers. The baby lay placidly, taking no notice. The Sister spoke to it, played with its hands and the little one laughed aloud. Radiant, the mother laughed back, and then the Sister disappeared to return a moment later—with another child. The young mother brushed past me, unseeing, flung herself down upon the ground and wept. I went away. I was sick at heart. Was this agony to come to Carita? I was shaken as never before. Even the giving up of Jane and the despair at finding myself a leper had not reached so deeply into the innermost recesses of my being. No son of mine should be born to that hell on earth, the expectation of becoming a leper. . . .

I did not leave the house for five days. José came but I refused to see him; the business could take care of itself. I drank steadily day and night. Tomas was in despair. He tried to talk with me; for the first time I laid rough hands on him and threw him out. Then Carita came.

She found me under the mangoes, unshaven, unkempt,

a whiskey bottle before me. When I saw her, my eyes cleared. I stumbled up and toward her and she put her arms about me. I had to know.

"Carita, tell me. Are you going to have a baby?"

"Oh, my poor darling! So that was it. Tomas came and told me about you. No, Ned, it's nothing like that. I really have been ill. Let us sit down."

I laid my head on the table and began to sob, great, tearing sobs. Carita sat there quietly weeping, and waiting. When it was over, she spoke.

"Ned dear; it is Christmas Eve." Christmas! I had forgotten time. I raised my head.

"Christmas," I repeated.

"Yes, Ned. Would you like me to remain and have dinner with you?"

"Dinner? Christmas dinner? Would you, Carita?"

I asked her to excuse me while I went into the house to shave and bathe.

Before I returned I went to where the blue orchids were growing and gathering several branches, shaped them into a corsage.

I rather self-consciously presented them to her.

"Oh, my darling—what an exquisite thing!"

"I'm sorry I have nothing else to give you for Christmas, dear."

"Nothing else! You pick your precious blue orchids and fashion them yourself into this bit of noonday sky. My dearest, I know what a gift it is. The memory of it shall remain as green as these leaves."

An hour later Tomas was serving us on the lawn.

The scent of the frangipani was heavy. Carita in her dark

gown with a lacy Spanish veil, was a vision of loveliness. I could speak now.

"Will—you will marry me, dearest?"

She sighed.

"No, Ned."

"But you love me—why?"

"You gave me the real reason tonight."

"I was a fool, Carita. But I will not be a fool again. Believe me; no son of mine shall ever be born."

"Yes, Ned. But, don't you see—that is the reason I cannot marry you. It is against the teaching of my Church."

"You can't mean the Church believes in bringing babies into this world to become lepers?"

"It is not for me to question."

"I want you, Carita. Are we to have nothing out of life, we who are doomed? I want you to marry me. We two could get so much out of life, together."

"Ned—you say we are doomed—but are we—or is one of us doomed, and the other not? If we had been married for years, and one of us recovered, there would be no question. But—if you were well and I remained ill—you would wish to go back to your home. And if I—no, I could never go back. Your people know so little of leprosy that they would accept you. But I have lived with leprosy all my life. If I could return I would be an object of distrust, of suspicion. I must stay here."

"Carita, it is not likely that I shall be cured. All these years the disease has progressed, slowly, but it has progressed. Why not snatch our happiness while we can?"

"Ned, let us face it squarely. I cannot marry you and arrange not to have children. That is against my faith and belief in God. You say life has nothing left. God is left. God is very real to me. He is a part of life."

I stared at her. In the moonlight her beauty had an almost unearthly radiance. Her glory was that of renunciation. I had no answer. Her way could never be mine. Bells were pealing, the old Spanish bells at the church, her church.

"It is but a half hour until the midnight Mass, Ned, the Christmas Mass. Will you go with me?"

We did not speak as we passed around the house and out into the road. There were many on their way to church. I did not want to talk, but if I had, the sight of the children, the younger ones running, laughing, and of the older ones—some of them hobbling along, would have kept me silent. Carita said nothing. As we passed from the shadows of the roadside trees into the moonlight I could see that she was deathly pale. I remembered that she had been ill and drew her arm through mine. The main road at the Colony Hall was full of people. We turned from the highway to go up into the old Spanish compound on the hill. The long, winding stone steps were a mass of kneeling worshipers. We slowly threaded our way among them through the stone gateway and entered the church through an exquisitely carved door. We stopped. They were singing. It was a fantastic, quavering song. Carita recognized it.

"Isn't that a stirring thing? It is one of the old barbaric shepherd songs. They are singing it this year for the first time. They have been practicing for months."

It may have been my mood that night but the music

caught me, enfolded me, and uplifted me. We waited until it was over.

Stone walls, stone floor, three hundred years old. Every seat filled with worshipers, every foot of standing room occupied. Father Marello was at the altar. He alone was well, the rest of us were lepers. Some of the musicians were nearly sightless, some without fingers. As communicants left the altar and went out of the church to make room, we moved forward into vacant seats.

After a few minutes Carita asked me to wait and went down the aisle to take her place at the altar. I sat watching the hundreds upon hundreds moving forward and back. On the faces of those returning was peace and happiness. Slowly I began to see that the Church was a vital part of their lives; in its communion they found strength to go on. It was nearing dawn when we finally went down the stairs and toward the house where Carita now stayed, the home of her cousin.

I was silent. But now I partly understood the hold the Church had upon its people, and why Carita, loving me as she did, could not change. I still held to my convictions, but I had gained a respect for hers. Marriage between Carita and me was impossible and would remain so. But there was no bitterness left in my heart. Falteringly, hunting for words, I managed to tell Carita something of this.

"Thank you, Ned. You are good to tell me. My heart is heavy, but it is at peace. That son of ours who will never be—he is thanking us tonight."

"Yes, Carita, that is entirely true."

We had come to her home and stopped.

"How do we go on?"

"I think for a little while it might be well if we met only in public, is that not so? Then, later, when we both have been a little healed by time, we shall manage a friendship. I do not want to lose you entirely, Ned."

"And I don't want to lose you, Carita."

"Then let us wait, until you are quite sure—and when you send for me I will come."

She lifted her face to mine and I kissed her.

"A happy Christmas, my dear." My voice was strange in my own ears.

"Good night, dearest. May the Virgin Mother bring peace to you."

I went home alone, more alone than I had ever been; knowing that I would be alone for all time.

CHAPTER ⁄ ⁄ ⁄ ⁄ ⁄ ⁄ ⁄ ⁄ ⁄ ⁄ TWENTY

By 1917 THE FISHERY BUSINESS WAS MAK-
ing a fair showing. We had built up a co-operative organization; each man drew a wage. It had begun with ten pesos
a month and had gradually increased to twenty. Profits
above wages were used to pay a small dividend. I had advanced most of the capital for equipment but soon, as each
man was able, he gladly invested in stock. Surplus profits
above the amount required for dividends were divided, forty
per cent coming to me. I took no wage and this was my
share as manager. The other sixty per cent of the surplus
profits was divided among the workers on the basis of the
total number of hours each man was able to work during
the month. By order of the doctors some men worked less
time than others, and each of the regulars was responsible
for a substitute who would take his place when he was
unable to work. As the years went on, I cut my share of
surplus profits to thirty per cent and finally to twenty per

cent. I took some pride in making money but really had little use for it. Since my place and my living were almost entirely paid for by my pension, these profits were set aside as a reserve.

José Cruz, who had modestly said that he had "assisted in the building of boats" proved a great asset to the company. Our first boat was sent from Manila, but after that he supervised the making of them all. We built one fairly stout motor boat and a number of smaller ones, outrigger canoes, which we used for going to the large traps set in the bay a short distance from my house.

The fish were easy to catch. Our traps, made of bamboo, resembled a circular picket fence protruding from the water. There was a wide opening at one end. Through this the fish entered, following along the converging sides until they passed through a small, funnel-shaped opening into the actual trap, a second enclosed bamboo structure from which they found it difficult to escape. We used hand nets to scoop them out from the inner corral, and dumped the catch into the boats.

I came to know our men very well. I spoke Tagalog readily and enough Visayan to get along. The younger people spoke English, since it was taught in the schools after the American occupation.

José Cruz and his daughter Maria lived in a small house not far from my own. José's wife had died before he came here. He worried a good deal about Maria. She was responding nicely to the treatment, however, and José hoped for her parole, even though it would leave him entirely alone.

Santiago Brillas, Victor Cabisan, and Ricardo Jacildo

(top) A native fish trap or "baklad."

(bottom) *Fishermen's houses and their boats.*

were young men, bachelors, and in the early stages of the disease. They were all good workers, but they lacked initiative, for they had been regular Plaza loafers. Jacildo and Brillas were fishermen by trade, however, and they eagerly joined the company and were of great service in locating the best places for traps. They also had an uncanny knowledge of the best spots for casting nets.

Francisco Umali was in his forties. He and his wife were both lepers. He was the one who showed the most rapid advance of the disease. So we asked him to accept responsibility for the nets. His wife joined in the work and the two of them made and mended our nets and occasionally helped with the cleaning of fish when we had an exceptionally large catch.

Our most remarkable member, Federico Arang, proved a conscientious and able fisherman. He worked with a will and almost at once his physical improvement was obvious. The doctors encouraged him to believe that he might be paroled. Arang responded with still greater improvement. We all eagerly hoped that the day of his release would come soon although his going would be a distinct loss to us.

I had initiated the business to save myself from thoughts of suicide, or madness, or degeneration. These three possibilities were only too real, as Winton well knew. Perhaps they were also real for the other men we employed. There was regular or part time work for nearly fifty, and the money was shared by wives and children, or dependents mostly outside the colony. The three bachelors now gave regular work to a man and his wife who did their cooking, cleaning and laundering. It was a small frog in a very big pond, but it was an active frog, and it started ripples. All the doctors approved, and claimed that the stores and other little businesses started by patients had been stimulated by our success.

Much of this I believe was due to Carita. She not only brought her own pupils to see our nets, and at times to see the catch landed and cleaned, but talked with other teachers of the school. They brought their pupils down in solemn classes, making our little company and its activities the basis for their teaching about the whole fishing industry of the Philippines.

The youngsters enjoyed it so much that I got Bruno Intong, an excellent wood carver, to make a number of small boats, which were offered as prizes to the boys and girls. The teachers used them as awards for essays written about the visit. Thus we were advertised throughout the colony and, as we grew successful, an increasing number of men applied for work. We could not begin to take them all, but I listed them and their qualifications. All this was reported to Dr. Winton. He used these listed men on colony work wherever possible, and saw that they were paid for it.

I thought I observed a tendency for the men who were occupied to take treatments more regularly. When they were idle it was much more difficult not to lose hope. I also had a feeling that those who were happily engaged remained in better physical condition.

It was about this time that we saw our first "parole." Thirty of the colonists had been pronounced "negative," that is, the disease had ceased to progress and they were considered to be no longer a menace. These thirty had been isolated in the "Negative House" just below the old Catholic church. Winton told me he took no credit for these "cures" since the majority were spontaneous recoveries. Leprosy like other diseases sometimes disappears of its own volition. These first paroles therefore were not significant from the medical point of view, but they were significant from the viewpoint of the lepers. This was the first large group to leave. It showed us that being sent here did not necessarily mean being sentenced for life. A man might have some hope of being discharged. And they who returned to the outer world would carry with them tales that should help in getting others to come without compulsion, which would be highly desirable, for it was a common thing for health inspectors to have to take a man by force, and many of these officers had been seriously wounded.

The colonists were not to be denied their fiesta and there was a great celebration as the thirty fortunate ones left.

The boat that took them off had brought a newcomer, an American and a Spanish War veteran, Walter Simpson. This was good news for me and when he had settled I went to see him. He was older than I, sandy-haired, stoutish and in a state of great depression. I did what I could to cheer him up, but he never did completely thaw out. He came from Pennsylvania, had been back in the States seven years before the disease showed itself, had first gone to Cebu, and that was about all I ever knew. We had one other thing in common. We had both studied engineering, but we seldom agreed heartily on anything, and I think both of us preferred the society of our Filipino friends to each other.

For a time Simpson took no interest in work whatever. I

didn't blame him for that; the kind of work I had to offer in the fishing business was none too alluring, and his outlook and mine were far apart. I let him alone a good deal. But he was an American, so I would send Tomas over from time to time with some special dish. Little by little he became more friendly—I think it was not in him to become very friendly with anyone.

Through the wireless station at Balala news reached us promptly. We were aware, by 1917, that the United States was about to get into the European War.

Jacildo and I were cleaning fish one day when, after a long silence, he brought his heavy knife down with a sharp blow on a pompano which lay on the table before him. The blade cut through and buried itself in the wooden top.

"I wish I were a well man. I would volunteer if the United States goes into the war."

A few days later as I was about to leave the Colony Hall shouts were audible from the lower road. A breathless boy headed a line of people rushing up the long flight of steps and gasped,

"America has declared war against Germany!"

Men threw up their hats and yelled. A boy on a bicycle came tearing down the street shouting there would be a rally in a half hour at the theater, "By order of the Presidente." A Filipino Paul Revere! Flags began to appear. I joined the shouting crowd moving toward the Plaza Libertad and we turned into the open air theater. At one end was an enclosed stage. There were rows of long wooden benches, all full, and along the sides people were standing eight deep. Pedro Cañete, President of the Leper Council,

Father Marello, and a few members of the Council were on the stage. When Dr. Winton joined them there was a burst of applause. The colony band filed in; the Presidente signaled to the leader, and they began "The Starspangled Banner." Ten thousand miles from home as I stood there, a leper among lepers, a lump filled my throat.

Was there, I wondered, anywhere in America, a meeting of greater significance? We sang the Philippine national anthem and Father Marello said a prayer. Then the Presidente arose. The Filipino is a born orator and nothing pleases him more than making a speech. Pedro Cañete spoke slowly, briefly, and with great solemnity.

"It is little that we, exiles as we are, can offer to our foster country in this time of trial. Perhaps by our good conduct and our willingness to aid ourselves we may release, for the service of the United States, a few of the physicians and nurses who now care for us.

"We must find comfort in the knowledge that were we free men and women we would be among the first to offer our services."

For an enchanted moment we were all enlisted, all a part of that army to march against the foe. Then it was over and the inevitable reaction set in. My spirits dropped. The men crowded about me—was I not an American?—asking all kinds of questions. How long would it take America to beat Germany? How many soldiers were there now in the United States? How many more could she hope to enlist? How about Germany's submarines, her navy, her air force? What had America to combat them? I answered as best I could. And I marveled at the amount of information these people possessed. The world was not dead to them! They were cheery to talk with. Not a one among them had any doubts concerning our conquering; it was just a question of how long it would take.

Insensibly my heart grew lighter. As I walked home and thought over that meeting, the spirit of these Filipino lepers seemed something of a miracle. Sixteen years before we had been fighting them; at the present time we were in residence as their governors. And yet in this crisis they were our partners.

When the first sale of Liberty Bonds came I expected to buy as a matter of course. I found that every person who could scrape together one hundred pesos bought a bond, and that when this was not possible several clubbed together and the bond was issued in the name of one, the others holding receipts for their share. The lepers of Culion had entered the World War.

As an officer in the National Guard, Tom was given some preference, and his prompt enlistment, together with this, gave him a lieutenant's commission. By the time I had his letter about it all, he must have been on the seas.

"If only we could have gone—together, Ned. I'll try to hold the flag for the family. Everyone has come back so far, so I suppose I shall. If I don't, I am sure you will be happier knowing that you need not worry about Jane. She is head mistress of a school of music in Chicago, and I understand doing very well. If anything happens to me you will be notified. I have arranged with Major Thompson. Bill is pleased as any lad. He has already returned to the Medical Corps."

I waited a long time before I got another brief note. Tom was in France; his regiment would see action soon. Another long wait and a note from Bill. Tom had been killed in his first fight.

I was miserably unhappy. Tom's death had turned thoughts to home. My days had been so full for several years that my old life had little claim on me. Now I was homesick. As I sat for hours at a time living through my earlier years I forgot how changed everything would be. I dreamed of seeing Tom, mother, Jane, Mabel, father even, then it would come crushingly back to me—all of them were gone except Jane and Mabel.

During these days Carita was a blessed refuge. We spent much time together.

Gradually she turned my thoughts back to Culion, which was now more than ever home for me.

For a long time I had been revolving in my mind the possibility of enlarging the colony's refrigerating plant so that we might supply light and power to the islanders. To do this we formed a stock company and sold shares to any of the colonists who could buy.

The prospect of a power plant quite brought Simpson to life. I offered him the Assistant Managership and he jumped at it. As fast as we could, we strung wires. Light bulbs and fixtures began to replace kerosene lamps. Equipment introduced new business, and as gadgets using electricity came into being, they were sold in the tiendas, the shops of which there were such a number. It was some years before we could generate power enough for all the things wanted, but small as the plant was it did give us plenty to do.

Also, I bought a small second-hand motor boat for my personal use. Tomas learned to run it and occasionally we would take a holiday. We took rods and lines and sometimes hooked the tender lapu lapu, or red snapper or pompano for our own table, or if we had luck, we fought a tanguingui or barracuda. And what a fight one of those wolves of the sea always gave us!

The two of us were just off Coron on the Culion Bay side one afternoon when a steamer came in sight. She was a leper-gathering boat from the East bringing new patients from Cebu and Iloilo. Just as the boat cleared the reefs there was a great commotion on board. We could see people crowding to the rail and looking down into the water. Someone had either fallen or jumped from the deck. I was at the wheel and I headed for the spot. Meanwhile the steamer swung about and lowered a small boat from the side. We were much nearer, and as we approached, Tomas, an excellent swimmer, leaped into the water and soon caught up with someone struggling there. The other boat came up in a few minutes and Tomas helped lift his burden in, then turned and swam back to me.

"It was a girl, sir. She jumped; she try to drown. The men in boat say she is very afraid to come."

I remembered how frightened some of my fellow passengers had been on my trip down. Since then Culion had become better known and it was not often anyone tried suicide any more. And suicide by a child, for so Tomas described her, was rare indeed.

Sometime later I asked Carita if she had seen anything of the little girl.

"She isn't so little," she said, smiling. "She must be all

of twelve years of age. Tomas saved her life, I understand, so let's ask him to come and hear the whole story."

I went to fetch Tomas who was busy in the kitchen. He joined us rather reluctantly. During the time since the rescue he had been kidded unmercifully by his fellows, and he had no idea that he was a hero. As usual, Carita's tact put him at his ease.

"The girl is Carmen Tolino, and she comes from the island of Mactan, a few kilometers outside the town of Cordova. You know Mactan, Tomas?"

"Oh, yes, Señora Torres. That is where the explorer and discoverer Magellan landed, and where he was killed; and they put up a monument to him."

"That was Carmen's home. But she has a strange history. When she was taken from the boat she still struggled madly and screamed. The doctors and nurses could do nothing with her. At last Nurse Villariosa, one of the Protestant nurses, did succeed in quieting her. When quarantine was over, Miss Villariosa accompanied the girl to one of the dormitories. It was from her, and a little from Carmen herself, that I pieced together the story.

"Carmen's father has a little pineapple farm, a poor farm because its soil lacks fertility. Carmen's brother Vicente is a leper. He was a leper when Carmen was born. But Vicente and his parents believed the wild tales about Culion. For over twelve years the whole family conspired to keep him from the notice of the health authorities. This was not so difficult at first, because behind their small house was a grove of coconut trees and palms. An open space back of that was all waste coral. At the far side, the coral rose into a broken and jagged hill, which cannot be mounted except on hands and knees. At its top is a narrow slip between the stones, well hidden by low underbrush, and back of this a cave, a natural hiding place. For all those years, Ned, years of fear and terror, Vicente fled to this cave to escape detection. When word would come that the health inspectors were on their way, Vicente would snatch some food and steal through the grove. His heart pounding, he would scale the hill and lie in the cave, straining every nerve at each unfamiliar sound. When the inspector lingered in the district and Vicente's supply of food ran short, one of the other children, in the dead of night, made the climb. Often, it was Carmen. Then the inspector would leave and Vicente would creep back to the family. Once when the inspector had stayed near them and she had not dared to go out, she had found Vicente nearly starved.

"She would not tell us all this until her brother had been discovered. When she was taken for the first treatment and saw the line of patients, the doctor holding a hypodermic needle, she again became hysterical. She is fine now. Vicente has been found and is in the Cebu leprosarium. He is to be sent here. When he comes, Tomas, he may be lonely. You have saved his sister, so perhaps he will be friendly toward you. Will you assist us by coming to meet him?"

"He is foolish man to hide," said Tomas promptly. "I think he will not listen to me. But I shall tell him the doctors here wish only to make us better. I shall say to him, 'Look at me. When I came here nobody could know—see me now. I am the same.' I must get tea."

It was Tomas's way of avoiding thanks and he went.

"Is the girl, Carmen, a bad case, Carita?"

"No, but the disease has already affected her hands a great deal. But she is very clever, and although her fingers have been partly absorbed she is able to do the most beautiful embroideries. If people were not so prejudiced, Ned, I believe that there would be no reason why such work could not be properly disinfected and sent out for sale. As it is there are no buyers."

Tomas came in with the tea and we fell silent. It was one of the comforting things about Carita that we could be silent, together. The sun had begun to set when she said, "Ned—I have some personal news. I—well, they say I am now negative."

"Carita!" I shouted. "Then you are cured! You are well and you can return to Manila."

"Not yet, in any event. I must wait a while. But, Ned, I told you once before that I do not wish to return, ever. It is too difficult. I am happier here, where I can work and be near you."

She was on the verge of tears and I knew I could not stand them. So I said hastily,

"Well, that suits me, Carita."

That evening as I sat and smoked I decided that if Carita passed the probation period and remained negative, somehow I would get her back to the world where she belonged. She was still young, there was much of life before her, she must return.

Nearly a year later Dr. Winton informed me that another group of paroles were to leave.

"Is Carita still negative?" I asked.

"Yes. I believe her illness is permanently arrested."

Shortly afterward she came for tea. I told her what Winton had said.

"You must not continue to live here. You are well. You must go back to the world where you belong."

"I am not going, Ned. I have told you again and again that I cannot face the suspicion and fear of the outside world. And I have work to do here. It is unlikely that I could find any among well people."

"If it is hard for you, Carita, what of the others? They have to face it. You may manage to stay, but Culion cannot keep all negatives. Some of them must return because they will be unable to find work, and have no one to care for them. But you have both your husband's people and your own. Carita, you owe it to those who cured you to go home and take up the fight for the paroles. Someone must find a way for them to be restored to normal life. You are well fitted to do this service."

She did not reply. Her lovely face reflected the anguish of an inner struggle. Evidently this was an idea she too had held, but had put away. As we sat silent, Father Marello came around the house. I rose to greet him. We three chatted for a few minutes and then I returned to the subject of paroles.

"Father, I am so glad you dropped in. I am trying to persuade Carita that she must leave Culion." His fine, old face expressed utter dismay.

"But Ned, Carita is my right hand. She is doing such good work in the colony."

"If Carita had come as Sister Victoire came, Father, I would have no ground for argument. Sister Victoire came to give her services, as a well woman, to lepers. Carita came because she had to come. She endured the horror, the despair, the hopelessness all lepers know. She has passed through this disease and is healed. She is a missionary of hope, a missionary of faith to the doubting world. A woman like Carita can make the outer world easier for those who will be paroled. It is not because I do not appreciate what Carita has done, but because I do, that I want her to go."

Father Marello was troubled.

"But, Ned, think of her work here. Think of the wives torn from their husbands whom she has helped to consolation. Think of the children torn from their parents whom she has brought to the infinite care of the Virgin Mother. Mothers, wrested from their children, she has guided to the compassion of the Infant Son." The priest was intoning as if at the altar. He paused. "I am getting to be an old man. Carita, can it be that I have become selfish? That I want your loving aid and presence when your work is elsewhere?" He bowed his head. None of us spoke for several minutes.

It was Father Marello who broke the silence.

"You will go, Carita. I have been blinded by my need. May the Heavenly Father forgive me. . . . I thank you, Ned."

Carita still held her peace. Her head was bent and her bosom rose and fell in short, panting breaths. I touched her arm.

"You remember Bernabe Crisolaya, Carita? He left here on parole, joyous in his return home. He had no one left except an old mother. Soon after he went back she died. He was picked up as a vagrant on the streets of Manila. He had to come back here to live. He has no right to be here, but we, here in Culion, could not help him in Manila. Perhaps you could have done so. Federico Arang is returning to his family. Where, and in what condition, will he find them? Perhaps you can help Federico. Carmen is going to follow you soon. How will she manage to live, with those remnants of hands? That kind of work is as worth while as anything you can do here, Carita."

She raised her lovely head. Her eyes were liquid with unshed tears.

"You—you want me to go?"

Every nerve in me cried out to keep her. But for me, all that was past.

"I want you to go. I want you to help us who remain to keep our dreams of returning. How can we keep them if we return only to be rejected? Unless this place is to become another Devil's Island where hope is surrendered at entrance, belief in return must remain with us. Every man who comes back undermines that hope."

"My son . . ." It was Father Marello. "In the years of your confinement you have increased in spiritual stature. Carita, you must not withhold from this friend the joy of your surrender. That joy is his because he is, in this, selfless." He paused and Carita, her eyes on me, faltered.

"I will go, Father."

Father Marello rose.

"I shall leave you two to work this out, my children."

For a time we did not speak.

"Where will you go, Carita?"

"Not to my husband's family, Ned. There would be no welcome there. I shall go back home. My father occupies a small public office in his province. They will receive me with joy and belief. But I do not know what I can accomplish for others. I fear that I shall be just another returned leper, shunned and avoided. . . . Ned, I shall come to dinner Monday. I am very tired."

I watched her down the path, and saw in her going the lean and lonely years ahead of me without Carita; without our long talks together; without her companionship at tea and dinner and the colony fiestas. I might be selfless, as the Padre had said, in advising her to leave Culion, but the sacrifice was almost too much for me.

Carita left on Thursday. With her went another dream of real happiness.

Walter Simpson and I were at the power plant, which now included our small refrigerating plant, a sawmill and the lighting division. We were going over a list of purchases to be sent to Manila. The two of us were standing outside the plant proper, near the tracks that ran out to a little pier where our boats unloaded logs brought in from the near-by islands to be made into lumber at the company sawmill.

A half dozen men were unloading the company's small barge. One of the inter-island boats lay alongside the pier at Balala down the bay, unloading a shipment of rice. The men working on the boat stopped and began to wave their hands and shout. There was a shrill blast from the steamer's whistle. We could see, from where we stood, a young lad racing along on a bicycle on the lower road of the colony and as he went past, doors opened, people came out, and confusion followed. As he passed through the gateway of the colony, the men standing about began running, following him toward the plant. When a Filipino runs, excitement is at fever heat. As the boy neared us he was shouting, although by this time he was gasping. Simpson got it before I did.

"Armistice! Armistice!"

Simpson dived into the plant and swung onto the cord of the big whistle. There was a swish of steam and then the scream of the whistle ripped across the colony and reverberated from the rocky side of Coron. Three times he pulled her down and another three and a third three, nine blasts. Then calling a boy, he gave the cord to him, and ran off to tell the fireman to keep up steam. The whistle on the lepers' light and power plant never stopped until the boilers were exhausted. I started up the winding road toward the upper level. Father Marello was at the church in the center of an excited group. He came through to me.

"Ned, this is a great day. Once again the cause of right has triumphed. But Freedom has been bought at a ghastly price. However, it has been paid for—and it is ours."

I knew that there would be a great celebration at the theater, already people were heading that way. They had stopped just long enough to dress up and to get out their American flags which they were waving. They were laughing and singing. But instead of following the crowd around by the stone steps to Plaza Libertad, I found myself going around the left of Colony Hall and along the road to my own house. Tomas was not there; evidently he had gone to the celebration.

Something had happened to me; I had to be alone. While the whistle screamed, something buried deep in me came to consciousness.

The shadows of the coconut palms were lengthening on the bay and it was cool on the porch. I went into the kitchen and brought out a bottle of Scotch, a glass and a pitcher of cooled water. I would celebrate alone. There was an idea within me struggling toward awareness, but I had many drinks before it raised its head so I could look it in the face, squarely. It was I, Ned Langford, looking at me, Ned Ferguson, and the inner man was insisting that I come to terms. I went out under the mangoes. What I had managed to hold on to—friendship, companionship, love—belonged there.

I rang the little silver bell on the table and waited for Tomas. He did not appear, he probably was still celebrating—the war was over. I went back to my brooding. Armistice was signed and Tom was dead. Bill must be dead too; nothing had been heard of Bill for months. I drank to Tom and Bill. They had a part in it and they had paid, gallantly.

The inner Ned Langford who had come into the open, was trying to tell me something. Everything seemed unreal. Maybe Culion and all of it was delusion and I had drowned in the river when the car turned over. I stood up, shakily, to drink to delusion. And then Ned Langford spoke:

"My armistice is signed, too. The fight is over."

Then I knew. Never before had I acknowledged it to myself, much less to any other. On the street and at gatherings I had taken to wearing gloves or to keeping my hands out of sight. Ass, to think that would fool anyone in this place! I held up the shortening fingers that had retreated to below the first knuckle. I held them out and jeered at them. I was very drunk.

"Come into reality, you fool! Good God!" I found myself laughing uproariously at the joke. I drank again, a toast. I shouted it. "To reality!"

I had seen men, at first a few, then more than a score, then more than a hundred, going away, apparently cured, and that kept hope alive in the rest of us who lingered on. I knew how we hoped against all the ghastly evidence of our own bodies—until death released us. Hope had deluded us, had trapped us to the end. I was done with delusion. I had lost out.

How we do cheat ourselves! Not only lepers but all men. We keep on hoping until we ourselves are ended. In that hour I faced it. I felt certain I would never leave Culion. I probably would not die of leprosy, but I would die a leper.

What was there left in life for me?

Across the bay I could see the shadow of one of our fishing boats. More rode at anchor. Below me were the piers, the plant—a small business to American eyes, a great one in Culion. Without friends or work, I had made both. I had prospered beyond anything which had been thought possible in such a place. I had the respect of my fellows. They sought my opinion—I helped them to live better material lives. Work meant more than the filling of the hours and the earning of money, although it was good, too, to earn money—for a leper. What they learned gave them a trade, something to do in the world of the well, should they be paroled.

The doctors did make progress; if not with me, then with others. My hands were going. Carmen's were worse than mine—and they said the disease might be checked—with her. No, not for me. I had other signs upon me. Stand up and fight, soldier. Get back to life! You cannot lie down—

not just yet. Sign up for duration—sign up with your eyes open. Sign up for what you, a leper, may be able to do! Sign before your hands have gone! I took up my fountain pen and signed in indelible ink across the top of the wooden table. There was nothing above the signature. But I knew. I had abandoned personal hope. I had work, I had power—I would live and work on.

Then I leaned back, well content. At last I desired to live. I had won my freedom. "He that loseth his life shall find it"—there was a law of compensation and Jesus of Nazareth knew it too.

Tomas came in very late.

"You did not come to celebrate the victory, sir."

"Not a complete victory, Tomas. An armistice, a truce."

"But that means no more fighting, sir."

"No more fighting, Tomas. No more running away. Getting on with the business of living—that is our armistice, Tomas. See,"—I pointed to the signature indelibly fixed in the table top—"I signed up."

CHAPTER ✦ ✦ ✦ ✦ ✦ ✦ ✦ ✦ TWENTY-TWO

Days grew into months and months
to years. It was three years after the Armistice that our little
colony was roused to fever pitch by the announcement of
a new Governor-General. During my stay here they had
come and gone with little excitement on my part. But this
man I knew. He was Leonard Wood, my hero of '98. Twice
before, he had been on the Islands, first as Governor of the
Moro Province and recently as a member of a special Commission of Investigation, on which he served with former
Governor-General Cameron Forbes. There were two things
about Wood that made his appointment of special interest
to me. I enjoyed the quite human satisfaction of knowing
that my particular boyhood idol still remained on his pedestal, and a much higher pedestal at that. And I was glad
that a man who had begun as a doctor was coming; it might
mean much for Culion.

One afternoon as I was working in my garden among

199

some orchids that would have taken prizes in the States, Dr. Winton called me. I laid aside my shears and, as usual, we sought the shade of the mangoes.

"Ned, I'm sorry to tell you that I am going home."

"Going home! Why, you've just come!"

"I mean back to America. I'm leaving Culion."

I sat back and stared. I could not think of this place without him.

"But why—and where are you going?"

"It's a new job, Ned. The State Leprosarium at Carville, Louisiana, is to become a Federal institution. They have made me its superintendent. It's on the Mississippi, near Baton Rouge."

"Yes, I heard something of the place when Major Thompson first diagnosed my case. Say, if you are going back, why not take me along?"

"I suppose you could go, Ned. And I'd like to have you. But, old man, do you know what you mean to Culion? Do you know what that business of yours means? Simpson can't run it; he is good enough as an engineer but he hasn't the influence you have. Who else is there? No, you can't be spared here yet. You don't really want to leave. Perhaps later you may. If that time comes we'll welcome you at Carville."

I stared steadily at my signature on the table top. My business . . . so it did really mean something; Winton recognized that. And he was telling me just what I had known when I signed up on the table top. The time was coming when I would no longer be able to work. Then I might go to Carville.

"We will postpone it then. When do you go?"

General Wood at Culion.

"I shall leave at the end of this week. I should like to remain longer, as the Governor-General has sent word that he is coming down. He is making the rounds now on his yacht, the *Apo*. But I am under orders and there it is."

I kept him as long as I could. I had a deep liking for the man and it was hard to see him go. A few days later we saw him off with great ceremony. I watched the boat out of sight. How I, all of us, would miss him!

The day General Wood arrived, there was a reception with speech-making. I had intended to go, but at the last minute could not get myself off. I didn't want Wood to see me, a middle-aged ex-soldier with mutilated hands. The men had been given a holiday except for two needed at the plant. I tried gardening, but it was no go. I got a small caliber rifle which I kept for target practice, went down to the beach and amused myself by taking a crack at bottles I tossed into the bay. Those I did not break in mid-air I tried to give the coup de grâce as they hit the surface. When I ran out of bottles I used small pieces of wood. I tried kicking them out of the water by a shot just under them and then catching them again as they fell, but that was beyond me. I was still at it when a deep voice at my side remarked:

"Good try! But I don't believe it can be done." I swung around aghast. There stood before me a powerfully built, bronzed man in an immaculate white suit, a white sun helmet under his right arm. I looked into the smiling eyes and kindly face I had last seen in an army camp almost twenty-five years before. He was alone. My bewildered eyes saw, back on the lawn, a little company of men, staff officers and some of the doctors of the colony.

"You should have been with the Rough Riders. Men who could shoot like that were right at home."

My tongue seemed thick, but I managed to speak.

"I tried to be, General."

What a mess. Here I was caught staying away from a reception to the highest officer in the Islands!

"Oh, so you did, did you? Well, why weren't you, then?"

My self-consciousness left me. I told him how he and I had met and my efforts to join him.

His face sobered. "You ran out on me this morning, but I've been hearing a lot about you. Heard about you in Manila from Marshall, Winton and others. So passing me up is out of the question. To punish you I decided to break in, and just to make it worse I'm going to beat you at this shooting." Here he turned and beckoned to an aide.

"Send out to the *Apo* and bring my small rifle."

The aide snapped to attention, saluted, and went off.

I indicated the great stone seat.

"It's clean."

"I wish to Heaven people would begin to look on leprosy with some common sense. Now how about this fishing business and the power plant? The doctors say the men working for you are happier and that their health has, if anything, improved. What do you think?"

"I agree, General. They earn money; it buys what they desire. They are happier and it reacts on their physical condition."

"I think you are quite right. It is horrible to deny people in a place like this the opportunity and joy of work. If we could do on a bigger scale what you are already doing it might benefit the families left behind. It would aid the government itself, relieving it of the heavy burden of the complete support of so many. It might make it possible for governments which cannot do what we are doing here to undertake work among their lepers. Your business is a pioneer work. In the future it may be so recognized. If I can help you at any time, don't fail to call on me."

"You encourage me very much, sir. As this undertaking has developed I have been increasingly certain that it has such possibilities. If leprosaria were located on land suitable for agriculture or manufacture, and if adequate aid were given in the way of expert supervision, I believe that, despite the inability of many of the patients to do more than light work, the colonies could supply most of their own needs. The consensus among the doctors seems to be that at least half the patients are able-bodied. It is true that outside markets are closed to them. But there is no reason why one colony should not supply fish, let us say, another rice, still another clothing, each specializing in what is most suitable for its own community. A plan of exchange could be worked out. At least the lepers' own markets should be open to them."

I glanced toward the house. It was evident that the group waiting for the Governor was growing impatient.

"Don't bother about them. Have you any other ideas on this subject?"

"Only this, General, and you know far more about it than I do. It seems unreasonable that there should not be some things which could be manufactured in leper colonies and sent into the open markets."

"What, for instance?"

"Well, there are such things as road materials: bricks,

tiles, concrete blocks, iron furniture, which could be easily disinfected. I have no doubt that an expert could find scores of articles which even the most uninformed would consider safe. Some time ago there was a scientist down here. I was discussing this with him. He suggested that alcohol could probably be made from the nipa palm. Certainly that would not be dangerous."

"Your ideas interest me, Ned. Keep this thing going. It's got possibilities. I've never been able to understand why people are so afraid of becoming infected with a disease whose point of infection is so low that we haven't been able to transmit it even by scientific methods in the laboratory."

He went on talking while we strolled about the house and yard. We drifted to fishing and hunting; we talked of barracuda and the wild boar and the small deer of Culion. The aide returned with the rifle. Wood spent the next few minutes giving as nice a demonstration of good shooting as I had ever seen. He threw sticks into the air and had little trouble hitting them. I threw some for him. Then he picked up a good-sized stone and threw it out. He missed and threw another. Again he missed. He picked a third stone with care, after rejecting several. He took his rifle in his left hand, which seemed a bit clumsy, threw the stone high into the air and fired. He missed. The ejection of the shell seemed almost simultaneous with the second crack of the rifle and a splinter flew from the stone, the bullet whining as it was deflected, the fastest and most accurate shooting I had ever seen. With a grin he handed the rifle to his aide.

"Better let well enough alone."

We joined the others and for a few minutes visiting be-

came general. Then they went around the house and along
the path to the road. I noticed that Wood had a decided
limp in his left leg, and I recalled the clumsiness with
which he took the rifle in his left hand. I knew he had suffered some injury during his stay in Cuba. This was the result. He was carrying on, limp and all. And he had come
and shown the limp to me, while I had stayed away. If
Winton had been there I never would have dared. . . .
The next time Wood came down—but it was no use. I was
thoroughly disgusted with myself.

CHAPTER ✓ ✓ ✓ ✓ ✓ ✓ ✓ TWENTY-THREE

My FRONT GATE OPENED AND I HEARD footsteps on the path. I walked to the edge of the porch, as two men came around the house. They were Americans. One was a huge florid-faced individual with a heavy mop of black hair, topped by a dirty, dilapidated, old tennis hat. He wore a none too clean and wash-wrinkled suit of dingy white. The second was a straight, slim and much younger man, bareheaded, with a spotless shirt of white opened at the neck, white riding breeches, equally spotless and pressed, and high tan boots polished to mirror brightness. His face and arms were bronzed until they almost matched the boots. He had an ingratiating smile.

"Red face" stared through me, and then turned and surveyed the yard.

The younger man spoke. "Good morning. You are Mr. Ferguson?"

"I am."

"My name's Lambert. Richard Lambert, and this is Pete Brant. Pete builds houses and roads up in Manila and one of these days I'll be practicing law in Philadelphia. Just now we are knocking around fishing and hunting, beating our way up from Jolo and Mindanao. We stopped off here last night. Some of the doctors told us about you and we thought we'd come up and make ourselves known. Hope we're not intruding."

"Gentlemen, I assure you, you are welcome as the flowers in May. Take the seats indicated, and avoid others."

"Baloney!" It was Red-faced Brant, and he had a voice like a bull. He dropped into the forbidden chair, looked at me ferociously and snorted.

"Hell, there ain't no danger. Since the war I've knocked about all over these islands, been mixed up with leprosy, cholera, smallpox and every other damned thing they have. Slept with the native women. Never caught a thing. If any man could catch it, I'd have got it."

"*I* did," I snapped. Lambert, who had stood by during this, now hastily took a visitor's chair. Brant was looking me over and he didn't miss anything.

"By God! That's right, you did! Reckon I made a 'fox pass' there. Well, I guess I'm just too tough. Guess that's all to the good this trip. Takes a tough hombre to tackle a tamarau."

"Tamarau?" I echoed. "You don't mean to say you're out for that beast? Why, he's almost legendary. No one about here has even seen one."

"Well, they don't grow here. But on Mindoro—that's the only place in the world they do grow." He lapsed into silence.

"Thunderbolt on four legs, I understand," said Lambert. "Boy, how I'd like to get one and take the horns home. S'pose I'd be lucky if I got home, after I met up with him."

We began to swap stories about tamarau. They were wild enough, and hardly to be credited. Taking your choice, the tamarau seemed to be a combination of unicorn and devil, plus a bit of typhoon—an onrushing animal that let nothing stop him. Then they began talking of the fishing business and the power plant.

"Must have nerve, feller," commented Brant, again running me over with his eyes. "Say." He turned to Lambert. "Let's take him along with us to Mindoro. Want to go?" He faced me without waiting for an answer.

My heart jumped.

"Why not?" Lambert argued. "I think it would be swell. Can you manage it?"

I thought swiftly for a moment. I was a model patient; I had been for almost ten years. Barring an occasional binge I had a clear record. Why not break loose once, just once? In a few years it might be impossible for me to handle a gun. . . . Winton had gone; my escapade could not reflect on him; the new man, whoever he was, had not yet come. It was now or never, for me.

"You would have to smuggle me on board."

"That's a cinch," Lambert spoke up. "Have one of your men run you around tonight. We'll pick you up just outside the bay and they'll have the devil's own time catching us, if they try. We've got a couple of Diesels that will get us out of here in a hurry. You'll be back in four days, five at most, and who will be the wiser?"

"Just every resident on this little island," I said wryly.

"Nothing ever happens here that isn't carried through the colony in a half hour. But what can they do? I'm in jail and I'll come back to jail. They don't hang us, here! I'd have to carry dishes and food. And I'd like to bring Tomas, my house boy, with me to get my meals."

"Got a couple of primus stoves, you can have one. How about guns?"

Tom's rifle, God bless him.

"I've a splendid gun, fortunately, a high-powered rifle."

"Good, we'll be expecting you." After they had left I went over the rifle, and added a repeating shotgun, and my revolver, important for close work if I were attacked.

The hours flew as I got supplies together and wrote out instructions for Simpson and José Cruz. In case my escapade proved serious in the eyes of the authorities, the sheets could be used to prove that the men did not know the nature of my journey.

José knew that we were going on some kind of jaunt, as he took us down to the cabin cruiser in one of our boats. But he did not know where we were going, and that let him out.

It was a beautiful night and all the guitars on Culion tinkled farewell as we boarded the trim little cruiser and she turned her nose up the west shore of Coron. Tomas and I had our quarters on a small after-deck. The others were forward on the spacious deck which combined with the bridge. Like a boy playing truant I stood there, my heart singing as I watched the path of foaming silver in our wake.

"How many in the crew, Tomas?"

"Four, sir. I think that Mr. Brant and Mr. Lambert have told them of us and that they will not come near."

About noon of the next day we ran into a narrow and winding harbor between precipitous banks that towered high above us. We dropped anchor some distance off shore. Mateo, our guide, was a Tagalog. He was a native of Mindoro and knew the likely spots for the beast we sought. I could see no signs of a settlement anywhere. The coastal villages of the island were scattered and the interior was almost unexplored, as far as the Filipinos and Americans were concerned. A primitive tribe of mixed Malay and Negrito blood roamed the hills, while the coast was settled by the more progressive Tagalogs.

During the afternoon Brant and Lambert took the small general-utility boat and fished. Tomas and I stayed on deck and waited. With the coming of night Lambert planned that we should go to the edge of the jungle, climb into trees and wait there until morning, when, as he seemed to expect, the tamarau would come up to be shot. Lambert had read a lot about tamarau.

Mateo, our guide, did not agree with his information: "It is not wise, sir," he protested, "to hunt tamarau in this manner. Many mosquitoes will eat you and the tamarau will not come. The tamarau is very hard to find. It is much better that you remain on boat and then tomorrow at daybreak we shall go to a very good place where tamarau go at night to drink, and then we can follow through the cogon." I was all for accepting Mateo's judgment. But Lambert held to his own view. As for Brant, he rumbled, "Matty knows what he is doing, Dick. I'm going to sleep while you perch in your trees like blasted birds."

"How about it, Ned?" challenged Lambert. "Will you come with me?"

Well, Lambert was my host and I lacked Brant's colossal nerve. I agreed to go. With severe disapproval, Mateo accompanied the two of us as we set off in the small boat, and landed on the rocky shore. We followed a stream up a gully, with the jungle all about us, and after walking an hour came out into an open region covered with cogon, a mixture of giant grasses growing waist to shoulder high. Mateo selected trees and each of us clambered up to a heavy limb and perched as comfortably as was possible. Silence was essential. In five minutes the mosquitoes had found me and proceeded to have the time of their lives. From all about me came howls and weird cries; jungle folk were abroad. The moon withdrew and we were in intense darkness. I wriggled and shifted and inwardly groaned. Some four hours later, Lambert called from the base of my tree:

"Say, Ned, come down. This is a washout." I scuttled down that trunk with a sensation of reprieve from torture. Mateo carried his head high as he led us to the boat. But he said nothing. Lambert was unusually silent. I was dead tired. When we got on deck I rolled up in a slicker and in two minutes was sound asleep.

We stayed in that spot three days before we saw our tamarau. Brant and Lambert grew impatient and wanted to move on. But Mateo was firm. The Americanos wanted tamarau; this was the one place they were likely to get tamarau. Mateo was merciless. He would rout us out before daylight each morning. He had prepared breakfast for the other two, and Tomas had mine ready. Then we were off, following the water courses, looking for the fresh trails that would tell us that tamarau had been there the night before to drink. Only two or three times did we find anything promising in the way of tracks. These we followed for miles. On one trail which seemed quite fresh we spent the better part of a day. We must have covered fifteen miles, wading through tall grass, fighting our way through jungle undergrowth, crawling silently on hands and knees for hundreds of yards when we thought we might be nearing our quarry. It was stifling. As we went through the cogon the barrels of our guns were so hot we could not touch them. Our hands were torn by thorns and scratched by rocks, and if there was one inch of me the mosquitoes had not tackled I didn't know where it was. It was beginning to look like a silly kind of play. My heart felt the strain. I wondered whether the lacerations on my hands would cause me future trouble.

Just when we were ready to give up, we found him. Tomas had wistfully watched us leave each day, so I asked if he might come along. I gave him my repeating shotgun to carry. It was loaded with slugs as a reserve. Mateo had no use for it.

"No good, sir, for tamarau." But I took it along nevertheless.

We were making for the open area beyond the jungle, pushing our way rather carelessly through the undergrowth. Lambert was a hundred yards or so to my left. The ground was soft and we made little noise. Suddenly dead ahead of Lambert three tamaraus started up and fled at terrific speed. We could see them, two gray—about the color of a carabao

—and a much smaller one, of a reddish color. Probably a bull, a cow and a calf. Lambert had jerked his gun to his shoulder and fired at the bull. We raced toward the spot and found splashes of blood on the grass and bushes. The beast was wounded! Lambert was wild with excitement.

"Did you see? It was the queerest thing. The cow ran her head under the calf and carried it, suspended on her neck. Some strong mamma! I never saw anything like it."

Mateo was impatient: "Wounded tamarau very dangerous. We must follow trail but must watch all time. Tamarau, he go long way straight. By and by he make big turn and come back. Wounded tamarau always fight. He come back. Must watch from sides, from back, from front."

Even Brant was impressed. "Hot time coming on the old island," he grunted. "Lead on, Matty."

But Mateo had not finished. "Tamarau not kill easy," he cautioned. "He hardest animal in all world to kill. It takes many shots. When he come shoot, shoot, shoot all time! Don't shoot when too far away. If he fall, don't go up to him until I say he dead."

Soberly we followed his instructions. He scattered us out through the jungle. The two animals had separated, so we had to follow two trails that were wide apart. I was on the one to our right and after a half hour or so of walking, found that Tomas and I were several hundred yards away from the rest. I felt a little safer out in the open than in the heavily overgrown jungle. The sun was hot and I slowed down. The trail grew fainter and was finally lost in the cogon. I began circling, trying to pick it up, Tomas at my heels. Suddenly he yelled,

"Look, he's coming!" I whirled around. The bull had

completely circled us. He charged at sight. I could just get a flash of that flat triangular head with its flat horns tearing straight at me through the cogon. I thought, "I've got to stop him! I've got to stop him!"

I dropped to one knee. The barrel stood steady as I drew a bead. I pulled the trigger slowly; I was working with cool deliberation. My first shot never checked him. I hit, but his head never wavered. On he came! I pulled again and again and again. . . . Four shots from that heavy rifle had gone into that skull and still he came on. I heard Tomas scream, but I could not hurry. He was almost upon me when I sent the sixth and last slug. I saw him hit the earth with all four feet sprawled, tearing a swath through the grass and hurling his gray dead carcass against me with such force that I was thrown onto my back.

By the time I had scrambled up, the others were there. Mateo did not have to tell me I had killed my tamarau. A quarter of his skull had been torn away. Mateo was right. No other animal in all the world could have taken so much killing.

When we stepped out of the small boat at the colony pier, I was greeted by a crowd that seemed to include every man, woman and child in the place. Word of the killing had preceded me, brought by a man who had seen the transfer of the remains of the tamarau from the cabin-cruiser, and had paddled in to spread the incredible tale. Mateo had skinned the beast and I had the hide, the cleaned head, and the horns. Men and boys crowded in close and asked to touch the horns. Tomas was kept busy acting as guard and both of us tried to answer the endless

questions as to the where, when, and how of the hunt. For
most of these people it was like discovering that the devil
himself had been slain. Here was the carcass—or enough of
it to prove the point—horns, tail and all.

Listening to Tomas I discovered myself to be a hero of
the first water. We handed the remains to Pedro Ramos,
who had been a taxidermist and who occasionally did work
in the colony. In about a week he brought me the head
and horns pretty well restored and mounted on a wooden
base. He took longer with the hide but finally it was cured
and I threw it by the side of my bed. Neither the hide nor
the head was likely to survive the insect life for many years.
Each morning as I walked on the rug with my bare feet I
got a distinct thrill out of the contact. I hung the head on
the wall of the house on the porch.

No official notice had been taken of our absence and we
had concluded that it was to be ignored, when one morning
Tomas came to me with a long face.

"Dr. Palao has sent for me," he reported.

Palao had been Acting Director since Winton's going.
The summons might possibly concern our escapade but it
was more likely that the boat that had just come in bore
news for Tomas. A summons like this usually preceded a
report of a death in the family. I told Tomas to hurry and
he was gone about an hour. When I saw him coming back
my lower jaw dropped and my mouth hung open. He was
hustling along, leading, or being led by, two fine German
shepherds. Respectfully following came a crowd of more
than fifty boys and men. Tomas, always dignified, looked
wild as first one of the dogs and then the other tugged at

the leash. I rushed to the gate to meet them, took the leash from Tomas, and found myself staggering under two pairs of paws, on my shoulders. Tomas fastened the gate, asking the crowd to please stay outside. I took the dogs into the house. They were mates, fine specimens, hungry and thirsty, but as gentle as kittens. After we had fed them, Tomas fished in his pocket and brought out a letter. It was from Pete Brant.

DEAR NED:
    You've got guts, as I said. Every man ought to have a dog. Shag and Mame are good stock. Pedigrees enclosed. See you again.

PETE.

CHAPTER ✦ ✦ ✦ ✦ ✦ ✦ ✦ TWENTY-FOUR

Before winton left he had supervised
the building of a Protestant Chapel with funds donated by
Americans, and had personally given the chapel a pulpit.
He had always hoped that some day there would be a resident pastor. That hope was to be realized. Reverend Hudson had been transferred from the Islands, and succeeding
him we had a number of others. Then Pastor Manson was
sent down from Manila. He had not been in the colony a
month before he and Father Marello were fast friends,
sharing together the problems of a sick people. In Culion,
at least, the preaching and services were only a part of a
minister's duties. The colonists went to the doctors for
medical advice, but they consulted our two spiritual leaders
for many of their personal problems.

We began to hear from that inspection visit of the new
Governor-General's. Leonard Wood the doctor was getting
into action. He was sending us an American scientist, who

would make an analysis of just what could be done toward making the colony more efficient. When he arrived we were greatly cheered. He was a man of distinction. For years he had been connected with the Medical School of the University of the Philippines.

Our first meeting was accidental. I was entering the clinic when Dr. Ponce, one of the medical staff, came out with a stranger. "Ned, I want Dr. Bond to meet you. This is Ned Ferguson, Doctor." His face lighted. "You are the man who shot the tamarau?"

"So they say," I replied sheepishly. At this late date was I to be blamed for playing truant?

"I want to see the head and hide, if I may. What a hunt that must have been! Brant told me something about it."

We talked on and on. It developed that he was fond of hunting, and that killing a tamarau had been a pet ambition of his own. He was not unlike Wood in general appearance, younger, and perhaps an inch shorter. He even wore his mustache clipped in the same fashion.

"I hope to see you within the next few days," he told me.

When he appeared at my house three days later he looked dead tired.

"How about a drink? Winton told me you were a good host."

"Can do; but come out under the trees where it is cooler."

Bond raised his glass—"Cheerio." He looked down to the coconut palms and the sea, then at the flowers and vines. "First place I've seen that looks anything like this. I wish they would all copy it. Culion has such possibilities for beauty. I saw the tamarau head on the porch. What a brute he must be! Anything worth hunting on this island? You know I may get down here to work, some day. If I come we'll do some hunting."

"That's fine. There are deer and wild boar."

Then he began on colony affairs. I told him of my pet hobby of suitable work for all able-bodied men and women, and a home life that did not involve bringing children into the world. He listened but offered no comment. Before he left, I told him that I hoped he would be sent down as Chief.

"I don't know. You see, my interests do not run toward administration. If Wood can get money for research, I would like to take a hand in it."

He seemed surprised and delighted when I warmed to that. Since my "armistice" I had done a lot of thinking and reading and had managed to look at leprosy with an almost impersonal interest.

"You are an unusual patient. Most of them run away from any knowledge of the disease."

"Well, I've had my own impulses to run away, plenty of them. I'm all over that. I know the answer for me; at least I am certain in my own mind that I do. Now I can read leprosy, talk leprosy and see leprosy without panic, and the result is I am deeply interested in the problem itself. Tell me, how did chaulmoogra oil come to be used for treatments—when did that begin? . . . Yes, Tomas?"

"Jacildo is here, sir. He has the plans for the new trap."

"Do have him in, Ferguson. Chaulmoogra is a long tale. I'll try to stop in here again in a few days. Just now I'd also like to see the plans for the new trap."

We called Jacildo in. That put an end to our conversation for the time being. Soon after, Dr. Bond returned to Manila, but I hoped, without really expecting it, that we had not seen the last of him.

Meantime, an unpleasant interlude was taking place. Carmen's brother Vicente arrived from Cebu. We had heard he was a malcontent and political agitator; kept stirring the patients up on matters on which he had no knowledge, and would be anything but an addition to the colony. As the disease had progressed pretty far before he was captured, there was little hope of his recovery.

Carmen herself was now seventeen and pretty as a picture, except for her deformed hands. According to Winton, there was every reason to believe that she would continue to improve and might be paroled. She was happy because of her brother's coming and enlisted Tomas to act as his guide.

After a week or two of trying to befriend Vicente, Tomas gave up in disgust.

"Vicente is a fool," he said shortly, when I questioned him.

"He may be a fool, Tomas, but he's got a mighty pretty sister."

Tomas nodded. "The sister does not make Vicente any better," he said gravely.

In two weeks Vicente had been all about the colony shouting for independence. I took it that he would have been quite willing to drive out the men who were making this place possible, men like Bond, and Wood—Wood, who was even then trying to secure more funds for Culion.

I met the fellow a couple of times and disliked him heartily. I never saw him when he was not surly and critical. He had what the doctors called the leonine type of countenance. The face of a lion—the trick that the heavy nodules induced by the disease frequently played—deeply furrowed brows, flabby cheeks, and large, thickened and elongated ears.

One day, Dr. Ponce told me Dr. Bond had accepted the post of combined Chief Pathologist and Acting Chief at Culion. I was delighted, specially since it seemed to mean that the Governor-General had accepted Bond's suggestions regarding the colony and that there was some real interest in leper citizens at Malacañan Palace.

Bond's return marked a real change in the spirit of the place. Plans were made for a number of new buildings for the treatment of patients, and for housing an increased medical staff. As a professor in the Medical School, Bond had the advantage of knowing the capacity of the former students there, and brought down from Manila Dr. Dominguez and several other young Filipino doctors as members of the medical group at Culion.

The new chief sent for me several times to consult about the working ability of various men I had employed. While patients could not be employed on the new houses being built for the Medical Staff in Balala, new dormitories, and some wards and clinics were planned for the colony, and they could work on these. I managed to persuade some of the able-bodied men who thus far had held aloof, that building a new Culion offered a worth-while field for any man's services.

When Bond had been with us about a month he came over and proposed that he and I go hunting. The deer on Culion are of a small variety and are hunted at night with the aid of lights. You tramp through the tall cogon until you pick them up by the reflection in their eyes of the light from the lamp strapped to your forehead—a sort of hunting that never appealed to me as sport. But since it was impossible to find the deer by day in the tall grass, I was willing to add to my own meat supply occasionally in this way. Sometimes a wild pig was bagged on a deer hunt but we usually hunted the pigs by day. As for the wild carabao on the Island, no one had as yet done more than catch glimpses of these huge beasts plunging through the jungle. No one even knew whether they were in truth wild carabao or descendants of domesticated animals which had been brought there long before the Island was set aside as a leper colony. I had never encountered one, and hoped that I never would. My tamarau was enough.

On this night Bond and I went out together. We pushed through tall, tough cogon and rough brush at the edge of the jungle for several hours with no result more formidable than a couple of monkeys who went off screaming and a gecko who croaked at us in puzzled but friendly fashion. Disgusted, we gave it up and went back. In returning to Balala, Bond had to pass by my house and I asked him in for a drink.

"Let's go down to the beach. I like to sit on the sand and watch the water at night."

We sat there for a long time without talking. The night was clear and warm and the air had that strange softness of the tropics. The tinkling instruments were silent, and even the colony dogs were still.

"I love nights like this," said Bond. "I was a northern man and when I went to a southern medical school, I fell in love with the South. That's where I met my wife. She's back there with her family tonight, but she'll join me when our house is finished."

I made no reply. I knew that he expected none.

After another silence he began. "You asked me once to tell you about chaulmoogra oil. I couldn't then. It is late, but maybe this is a good time. At least we are not likely to be disturbed!"

"Time is all alike to me. In this little spot out of the real world we live a kind of suspended life. Time does not count."

He took out a cigarette, fitted it into his black holder, held a silver lighter to it.

"My wife sent me this . . . rather nice, don't you think?"

"It's exquisite."

"This business of chaulmoogra oil goes back a very long way. It has its beginning in a legend; a highly incredible yarn that has persisted through the ages. The story is that a certain prince of Burma became a leper. When his condition was known, he was banished to the jungle. But the love of life was strong within him and he lived on, eating what he could find, fruit and nuts. He came to the chaulmoogra tree—the true chaulmoogra grows almost exclusively in Burma—found the fruit, opened it, and ate of it. But I can't imagine the taste was any too pleasant. You probably know something about that."

I told him of my experience with it in New York and shuddered. "It's a horrible taste, Jack. Take it from me that prince must have been starved."

"And at that you didn't get the real chaulmoogra. What is used in America and here is the hydnocarpus, a kind of cousin, that grows in many places. To get back to our prince: he ate the fruit again and again, and in time his leprosy diminished and finally he was cured and returned to his palace and forthwith publicized chaulmoogra as a cure for leprosy.

"You can take the yarn or leave it. About all it really means is that chaulmoogra has been identified with the treatment of leprosy for hundreds of years. The fact is, it's the oil from the nuts we use, rather than the fruit itself.

"On my way out to the Philippines I visited Indo-China. I went to that old, jungle-buried city of the Khmer kings, Angkor-Tom, near the famous temple of Angkor-Wat. The Khmer kings date from the first century A.D. Angkor-Tom had a million inhabitants, with magnificent temples and the royal palace, and, at one time, it is said, a king who was a leper. The city itself is in ruins, except for a few temples and the royal palace, which are reasonably well preserved. Near the palace is 'The Terrace of the Leper King,' to which the ailing king presumably was banished. The terrace is surrounded by a stone façade decorated with reliefs of panthers, elephants, tigers and scenes of battle. And mingled with all the rest, the figure of a tree, which the natives of today tell you is the chaulmoogra tree, symbol of hope for the leper.

"So chaulmoogra is lost in the mists of antiquity, and still we moderns have not found anything better to use in treatment. We have improved the forms in which the drug is administered, but the base is the same old remedy. In the search for something better, experimentation has produced some freak results. Aniline dyes have been experimented with; methylene blue has been popular with some doctors. Unfortunately with that drug the patient turns a nice shade of blue, and remains that way for a long time. Each time something new has been abandoned, we have gone back to the ancient remedy. . . . Am I boring you?"

"Far from it. Please go on."

"One of our great problems is to find a cure. There is a vast difference between work for lepers and work against leprosy. In the latter, research is the thing that counts. I want to see this ancient curse removed from mankind. We must take care of its victims. That is a measure of humanity. But we must end leprosy! It is estimated there are three million lepers; only three per cent of them receive any care. They are found in practically every country on earth. Leprosy is found in Iceland and Norway, India and Africa. It drags its victims down to utter despair and it burns a wide swath of destruction among those not infected. A man becomes a leper. He has a wife and children. Without warning he is taken away. They are left."

I thought of Federico Arang, the lawyer, who worked with me. He would leave on the next parole. All Arang's money had gone to his family. Had it been enough? What was he going to return to?

Bond was speaking again. "I have gone far beyond my own part of the problem, Ned. What is to be done for those who are left is, or should be, the problem of the government that removes the breadwinner. My work is to find a stop and a cure for leprosy. We must tackle the problem on a new scale, with new equipment and deeper research. We know so little. We do not know why one member of a family becomes a leper and often the others do not. Our cures, if you can call them that, seem hit or miss. We know that the disease burns itself out in a limited number of cases. That is, the patient recovers without any treatment. We give treatments to two men in exactly the same stage of the disease. One of them responds and is cured, so far as we know. The other, who has been just as faithful in following advice and in taking treatment, goes steadily on and becomes an advanced case."

"Yes, Jack, I know that to be true."

"I'm sorry, Ned. I forgot about you. We have a long way to go. In fact we've just begun. Even when we send a man out as an arrested case he hasn't better than a fifty-fifty chance that he won't come back. We are not going to stop until we've found the answer."

I sat there long after he had gone, turning over in my mind what he had said. Was he right? Would all this misery some day come to an end?

ON MY WAY TO THE PLANT ONE MORNING
I encountered a small group in the middle of the road with
Vicente in their center. He was in the midst of an impas-
sioned speech.

A few men and six mangy dogs were there when I arrived. Little by little a crowd gathered. When I heard
phrases like, "white usurper to be cc-rrushed," I ground my
teeth and had hard work to restrain myself from going in
and wringing his ugly neck. I stalked off through the crowd.

Conrado Miguel was coming hastily toward me. He was
one of my fishermen. He was a good if somewhat temperamental worker.

"Mr. Ned, will you help me?"

"Certainly, Conrado. What is it?"

"It is necessary that I go to court. It is that Marciano
Santez has reported an occurrence."

"What occurrence?"

"Please, Mr. Ned, there is not the time to tell you. If we are to be there when Marciano appears we must hasten to the courtroom."

Our community had almost an autonomous rule. The Chief of the Colony represented the government. The making and administering of the local laws and the preservation of order were largely in the hands of the patients. We elected our own council as well as our police force.

The Civil Court of the leper colony was conducted in an upper room of the Colony Hall. The cases were petty ones, but the patients derived a good deal of entertainment from the show, especially when lawyers were engaged. There were no lawyers this morning, but the room was well filled. Sheepishly I followed Conrado to the front of the room and sat down.

Dr. Morales, who was Acting Chief, smiled at me from behind the rail. He was disposing of a claim of one of the lavenderas. She had not been paid the amount agreed upon. Finally Morales managed to get the woman and the man for whom she worked to come to a compromise. Then he called,

"Marciano Santez against Conrado Miguel. Will the principals please step forward?"

"It is about the pig, your Honor," began Marciano as he started for the railing that separated the Justice's seat from the courtroom proper. "I possess, your Honor, a very fine boar which I regard as a source of revenue, giving service to such of those members of the colony who possess sows worthy to be mated with this fine boar. This service is rendered without cash payment, upon the assurance that of the litter resulting, I, as owner of the very fine boar, shall receive one half, fifty per centum for services rendered. Now it has so happened, your Honor, that the sow of Conrado Miguel brought forth a litter of nine sucklings who remained with the mother to an age when they might be removed from her care with safety. Forthwith Conrado Miguel brought to my dwelling four pigs of the issue of his sow and my fine boar. But when I inquired concerning the fifth pig, he refused to deliver it to me."

Dr. Morales cleared his throat.

"Did you have any agreement, Marciano, as to the ownership of a pig of the litter, if said litter happened to be an odd number?"

"We had no agreement," Conrado broke in passionately. "But every country on earth recognizes the right of the mother to her progeny, as superior to that of the father. The last pig of the litter was a runt. It was due to the mother's loving care that he survived and flourished—"

"The right of the father is also recognized," broke in Marciano. "The Napoleonic law gives first right to the father, as well you know, your Honor."

I was rolling with suppressed delight. They must have boned up for that court scene. Morales kept his face straight with great effort.

"Suppose that the court appraised the value of the remaining pig," Dr. Morales finally managed. "And that Marciano bought the half of the animal which it seems is Conrado's due."

"I do not possess the means, your Honor," snapped Marciano.

"Well, then, Conrado, suppose that you purchase that half of the pig from Marciano."

"I cannot abandon my conviction of the rights of maternity, your Honor," said Conrado firmly.

There was utmost confusion in the courtroom. Every patient attending was discussing the right of pigs' maternity and the Napoleonic code. Filipinos are greatly impressed by any show of learning, and Conrado and Marciano would both henceforth have new status in the colony. Both were aware of this and their faces lost belligerency and assumed a kind of complacent satisfaction.

The gavel of Justice Morales rapped sharply for quiet.

"I have taken this case under advisement," he said with great gravity. "I am about to suggest an equitable solution. I propose that Marciano and Conrado kill the young porker, and that they divide him longitudinally into two equal parts, each family to celebrate the addition to the litter as a gift, and have lechon."

The gaze of both Conrado and Marciano traveled back through the rows of eager faces in the courtroom. Evidently they were seeking counsel of their wives. Suddenly Conrado's sober countenance lightened.

"I accept, your Honor."

"And I, too, your Honor," added Marciano.

"The court declares a recess," said Dr. Morales hastily.

They filed out. Conrado waited at my side and thanked me for my attendance.

"Good luck to your lechon," I responded.

Then I joined Dr. Morales, and we laughed until we ached.

"Pigs, the Napoleonic code, the rights of maternity," he said. "Oh, what a morning! I shall never despair of the future of my countrymen."

"And what of the judge?" I demanded. "Solomon had nothing on you, Doctor. I had thought of offering to buy the pig, but yours is by far the better way."

We had our lechon. I say we because late that same afternoon Marciano and Conrado, their friendship restored, called to invite me formally to the pig roasting. Their party was held on the beach. I arrived just as they were giving the finishing turns to the porker which was run through by a long pole and suspended by two forked upright posts on either side of the fire. Amid much laughing and joking the two men brought the pig to the wooden table and removed the pole. It was cooked perfectly. The skin was a golden brown, the fat was still dripping. They gave us an appetizer for the meal, pieces of the brittle crust. No more delicious thing can be imagined than Philippine lechon as done by an expert, and there was no doubt our two chefs were all of that. The womenfolks had prepared sweet potatoes and vegetables as well as cakes.

"Dr. Morales," I remarked, "was even a better judge than Solomon."

"DECORATED ON THE FIELD OF BATTLE."
Who of us that sailed on the old *China* over twenty-five
years before had not dreamed of that moment when the
regiment would be called to order and before its silent rows
the Colonel would pin to his jacket the medal that would
tell to all people for all time that he had been "gallant in
action"? It had never happened to me, but I had dreamed
of it, often. We had our field of action, a battlefield no less
desperate than that of war. There were few decorations in
that long, deadly struggle, but there was at least one: Word
came to us one day that Sister Victoire was to be decorated
by Governor-General Wood for her long years of faithful
service. That was a man who recognized gallantry in action.

All of us loved Sister Victoire. Her kindly eyes and her
imperishable smile made her a beautiful woman. She came
from Chartres in France, and she had been at Culion since
its beginning. She and a few other Sisters were sent here to
prepare for the first boatload of patients.

Wood made a short speech when he presented the medal: "Sister, I stand before you in a double capacity. I am one in spirit with those who live here and who wish to express their love for you and their gratitude. I also represent these Islands you have come to bless, and the country which in the beginning made this work possible. In both capacities I am honored to be the bearer of this medal, prepared in recognition of your years of unbroken service. . . ."

Victoire looked down at the gold medal Wood was pinning on her white garb and smiled that strange sweet smile we all knew.

"Thank you, my dear Governor-General. Thank you and everyone else."

After the ceremonies Dr. Dominguez, who had recently been appointed our Chief, accepted an invitation of several days' standing to visit me. There was a quality about the Filipinos which I liked. They were formal and reticent. They would never come to my house for a visit except on invitation.

I had taken a great liking to Dr. Dominguez. Bond, who had resigned as Chief because of his increased responsibilities, approved the idea of a Filipino as administrator of the colony and I thought he was right. The Philippine government supported the place and aside from Walter Simpson and myself, all the population came from the Philippine Islands. They were almost entirely Filipinos, Moros or Chinese.

We were lucky to have a man of Dr. Dominguez's capacities and spirit. He was genuinely interested in the problem of leprosy and conscientious in his responsibilities. He had not been here a great while before he began experimenting with a new method of treatment by which the chaulmoogra was injected directly into the lesions. This was done in addition to the regular treatment of injecting the drug intramuscularly. The results with many patients were startling. The lesions almost wholly disappeared.

Dr. Dominguez was a man of rather striking appearance, taller than the average Filipino. He came briskly through my gate at exactly the hour we had agreed upon. He had visited me on a number of occasions and always arrived just on time. My associates in the business were studiously unpunctual. At least it always seemed to me that such invariableness could have been achieved only by careful planning. If an appointment was made for three o'clock with a man like Jacildo and he arrived at 3:59 he answered any protest by pointing out that it was not yet four. It must therefore be three, the very hour we had fixed. "Philippine time" it was called. "American time" was the absurdity of meaning by "three," sixty minutes after two.

Dominguez joined me in the yard.

"It's pleasant to come here, Mr. Ferguson. There always seems to be a breeze. I don't believe there's a spot on the Island where you can escape the heat as you can here. I assure you it's much better than Balala. Day or night it's pretty hot there, even for the tropics."

"Others have told me the same thing," I replied. "Well, I hope you'll come up to cool off whenever you feel like it."

We sat in the shade. Tomas brought us bottles of orange drinks. The Filipino rarely drinks hard liquor other than the native tuba: the fermented sap taken from the bud-bearing stocks of the coconut trees and drunk mostly by the poorer people.

"That was an impressive ceremony this morning, Doctor."

"Yes, wasn't it? Sister Victoire and her associates, and the Protestant nurses have done a wonderful service. I don't know how the doctors and regular nurses could ever manage with so many were it not for them."

"Do any of these well workers ever get leprosy?"

"Almost never. Taking it the world over, hundreds, thousands, I suppose, have worked in leprosaria. The instances of infection, so far as I know, could almost be counted on one hand and yet some of these places are two or three hundred years old, like San Lazaro."

"Then why are people so afraid of the thing?"

"That's something I've never understood. The disease is mysterious, but this universal revulsion is more so. There are plenty of things that look as bad or worse than leprosy. An advanced case of syphilis, for instance, or yaws. And then there is the fact that it is so difficult to transmit it, despite the fantastic tales we hear of people getting it from a letter or a Chinese laundry. The fact is that we can usually trace the source of infection back to something far more significant and more credible than such casual contact.

"A few years ago a case developed here. The man was a clerk who exchanged the Philippine money of new arrivals for colony coinage. At first it was assumed, as a matter of course, that the fellow got it from exchanging this money. Later we learned that there was leprosy in his family. He probably had leprosy when he came here."

"Is nothing known about how it spreads?"

"Not with scientific certainty. We do have some definite opinions growing out of our observations. We feel fairly sure that it results from long, close contact. We find, in two places near each other and seemingly quite similar socially and economically, one with high incidence and the other with little or none. It is an amazing observance, testified to by leprologists in different parts of the world, that the case of a wife contracting leprosy from a leprous husband, or the reverse, is rare. The general estimate seems to be that it is not more than five or six per cent."

"Have there ever been any ideas advanced that it is caused by living in the tropics, or from food?"

"Various ideas have been advanced from time to time. While it is true that the larger incidence is in the hotter climates, it is, on the other hand, found all over the world. Theories have been suggested, have even been believed, that some kind of food was responsible. One man firmly held to the idea that it came from eating fish. Scarcely anyone takes that seriously today."

"But, couldn't it be carried by cockroaches, bedbugs or some other insect?"

"Yes, it could, of course, and we may some time find that it is. However, attempts have been made to find the leprosy bacillus in insects that have intimate contact with human beings, insects like flies, mosquitoes, or bugs. No evidence has been found that any of these, though they were in contact with known open cases, were carrying the germ."

"Still, mightn't they?"

"Certainly. That doesn't rule them out. If one of these is the culprit or more than one of them, I suspect it will be found to be a kind of insect which remains in the house and does not travel far. This might explain why the disease will claim a number of victims in one house and none among the neighbors."

"Is there no way to find out about these things, Doctor?"

"Yes, I'm sure there is. As an epidemiologist I believe that field studies may give us some more definite clues. I think we should take areas in different parts of the world where the conditions differ and make a complete clinical examination and study of the family histories of all in these areas. These studies should be made both in regions where there is much leprosy and where there is little. Especially where such areas are close together and similar in types of people and habits of life. We should take into account food, climate, general living conditions, prevalence of other diseases, possibly those that have a tendency to diminish physical resistance. These insects we mentioned and others should come under the microscope of such studies. We should ignore no factor which could possibly contribute to the transmission of the disease."

"But that will take a long time."

"Yes. It might take the lifetime of many men, but suppose it does, if it promises to give us some real information? It has to be faced as a long effort but I for one don't believe that there's a single malady that can't be wiped out if we set ourselves to do it."

His words, the fire that burned in his eyes, the prospect he painted, the possibility that the time might come when men and women no longer would be snatched from life by this thing moved me deeply.

The shadows of the palms were long as he rose to go.

Mrs. BOND CAME TO TAKE UP HER RESI-
dence on Culion as soon as their house was completed.
She was young and attractive. She was also a writer and
her poignant stories of life in the colony were published
in various journals in America. When Governor-General
Wood decided to make an appeal to America for assistance
in extending the work for lepers and against leprosy, he
sent for Mrs. Bond. She went to Manila and Wood asked
her if she would go to the United States and make the
appeal in his name. When she agreed, the colony was jubi-
lant.

In 1927, Wood went to America on leave. He never returned. The old injury suffered in Cuba proved fatal. After
his death, the campaign in behalf of leprosy was carried
on as a living memorial to this great man. At first slowly
and then with accelerated momentum, America answered
the appeal. Scores of patients were engaged to build a new

road to run back into the hills, a road that would pass through the jungle and make certain arable land in the interior available to lepers who wanted to become farmers, and who still could come into the colony center to attend the clinics or get supplies.

Down in Balala more houses were going up for doctors who were to come to Culion for intensive scientific research. Homes were built for technical workers who would serve in the laboratories. A much-needed home for nurses was under construction. The first call went out for men and women patients to act as assistant nurses; the regular ones were worked to exhaustion. The colony was still growing; in 1926 there were over five thousand patients. A part of the new funds went to pay these assistants and this meant more employment for the colonists. One hundred patients were thus given work.

On the hill just back of Number One Hospital the ground was being cleared for a new laboratory. I had visions of this laboratory with doctors, Americans and Filipinos working side by side, and then of that great day, that day to come, when they would raise their heads to announce to an awe-struck world:

"We've got it! Leprosy is dead."

One Saturday night I was walking about the yard with my police dogs Shag and Mame, wondering about Carita and how she was faring. Bond burst in, panting. There was a cable from Mrs. Bond in his hand. He held it out to me:

FRIEND OF WOOD GIVES HUNDRED EIGHTY THOUSAND CEBU LEPROSARIUM AS MEMORIAL WHEN START WORK CABLE

Bond had often spoken of Cebu, an island to the east of us, containing the city of Cebu, the second largest city of the Philippines. His idea was to build a model leprosarium there, in the most densely populated of the Islands, where leprosy was endemic, and from which the majority of cases at Culion came.

"Ned, next to paroles, a leprosarium at Cebu will do more than anything to remove from people the terrible fear of being found leprous. You will see. We shall have volunteers for treatment, instead of having to arrest them and to bring them in by force. There will be no more tales, tales that are horribly true, of health inspectors cut to pieces by bolos in the hands of frenzied lepers. There will be no more innocents knifed by neighbors because they have been suspected of having given information as to the whereabouts of a leper in hiding. We are going to change all that.

"Cebu Leprosarium will be near the homes of the people who are ill. Their relatives can see much of what is going on there. This terrible isolation, far from the beaten paths, will end."

It came to me in that moment that the day would dawn when the leper would no longer be treated as a criminal and exiled to places as remote as this one.

"I understood," I said, "that you had no flair for administration!"

But Bond was too happy to take me up. "Here is something else we are going to do. The old leprosarium at Cebu consists of a number of nipa houses which are utterly inadequate. When the new leprosarium is finished, we will get rid of them all, and in their place build a modern clinic for the treatment of any kind of skin disease. At the same time it will help us to find leprosy in the early stages, and finding it then, we can hope to do something about it."

My mind flew back to my first spots. How long I had them before anyone recognized what they were! Had they known . . .

"I get you," I said soberly.

It was growing light and the earliest cocks had begun their infernal racket when he left. I had just fallen asleep when someone shouted outside my window. It was Jack Bond's house boy, Socorro, with a note.

> NED: A message from Governor-General Stimson was waiting when I got back. He knows of the gift and two army planes are being sent down to take me to Manila. Is this real or have I gone nuts?

"Socorro," I shouted. "Tell Dr. Bond this: 'You're damned lucky. Will see you off.' Got it?"

"Yes, sir. Mr. Ferguson tells you, you are of the accursed fortunate. He will be seeing you." I got him straightened out at last. It was broad day.

I stood on the high ground overlooking the bay and, with all of the thousands on Culion fit to leave their beds, watched the two graceful army planes swoop in from the north and taxi up to the pier at Balala. Dr. Bond and Dr. Dominguez, in their immaculate whites, walked briskly down to meet them. The officer on the pier saluted. Bond and Dominguez climbed in; the planes taxied across the bay and just as they hit the early morning shadows of Coron, they lifted slowly, skimmed the high crest of the

Island, and disappeared. I was swollen with pride. The army was in this game too.

Bond was gone for several months. It was late fall when he came back, still excited and full of news. He and Dominguez had tramped over miles of hills and valleys and jungles to find a site for the new leprosarium and had finally fixed on a spot a dozen kilometers outside the city of Cebu. Work had started. Pete Brant sent me a "hello." He was the contractor in charge of construction.

The constant running about from plant to house to Colony Hall and back again was tiring me. I wanted a car. In these days of so many kinds of autos, buying a car was a puzzle to me. So I wrote at once to Pete to get me a small, inexpensive car and to make his choice. Within a few months it came, an up-to-date model of the universal make. Only Pete had selected in place of the usual black, a deep maroon, much the color of our first auto at home, the one they retrieved from the river in New York. Cars were a novelty in Culion. Bond was the first doctor to have one.

All through my years on the Island I continued to report regularly for treatment. In this I had a double purpose. The doctors assured me that it had a good effect on other patients who, after some time, might be tempted to give up the struggle. And I myself had a suspicion that although the disease was slowly progressing, the treatment might have retarded its progress. We had gone through several phases of the treatments and I had received injections of the pure chaulmoogra oil, then a mixture with camphor, and last some new esters which had less unpleasant results. By this time I was seasoned to any and all of them and rarely indeed did I have any reaction worth mentioning. Sometimes I had a dizzy spell an hour later, but it passed within a short time.

One morning I was going in for treatment when I saw a girl in the corridor talking with Dr. Ponce. Even at that distance I sensed something familiar in her appearance. I noticed a bouquet of flowers held in her hands. I hastened to speak with her, but she turned and saw me, and in apparent confusion hurried away. I tackled Dr. Ponce.

"Wasn't that Carmen, Doctor?"

"Yes, Ned."

"What on earth is she doing here? She hasn't had a relapse, has she?"

"No, indeed. I went over her myself just a few days ago. She is in most satisfactory condition. She came back on some personal business, I believe. Her father died. And you know her brother, Vicente, is here. Excuse me, please, I am due at the clinic."

Dr. Ponce was evading me. There was some mystery here. Why had not Carita written me about Carmen? I went to the post office. There were two letters. One was from Carita, a gay, chatty little note. How were things going in the business? How were Tomas, Shag and Mame? She must get back to see us all, but she was so busy . . . that was all about herself, and not a word about Carmen.

The second letter was from Bob Sellars.

There was an American here recently, named Pete Brant. He told me an incredible yarn about your killing a tamarau. I suppose it really did happen. My congratulations. Ned, I was pretty low when you last saw me, but much has happened since then. I have a fair enough job

at Benguet. My wife and the children have moved here
and she likes it. You did buck me up a lot and I shall
never forget it. I am enclosing a postal order for the
money which you gave me. I'm sorry to be so long in
returning it but it really saved my life.

Good old Bob, I rejoiced in his turn of fortune. When I
arrived at the house, Tomas was nowhere about. I found
him on our "ground floor." Books and pamphlets were
piled on a table and he was hard at work. He looked quite
embarrassed when he saw me.

"Please, Mr. Ferguson. I like very much to know how
you understand to run business and to keep books. The
Chief Clerk has given me a few books on figures and accounting. I study all the time I have. You do not object?"

"Object? Far from it. You have been a good manager for
me, Tomas. I can easily believe that you would make a
good bookkeeper and accountant. I will help the good work
by coaching you myself."

"Thank you very much, sir. I accept with pleasure and
gratitude."

"Oh, sir, I have completely neglected my duty. José Cruz
has been here and wishes to consult with you at the plant.
I am most sorry, sir. Please to forgive me."

Down at the boat landing I found José. One of our fishing boats was leaking and needed immediate attention. By
the time that was set right Carmen had faded entirely from
my mind.

CHAPTER ╱ ╱ ╱ ╱ ╱ ╱ ╱ TWENTY-EIGHT

VICENTE WAS PROVING A DANGEROUS TROUble maker. His malcontents were increasing in numbers so that there had grown up a gang averse to work but not to talk. They were continually ranting against everything from the American government to the lowliest health service clerk. For years we had been a peaceful community, surprisingly so considering the thousands of us. Incorrigibles were few, but they were adding to their number weaklings who were easily influenced by hot-air oratory. Not a single one of Vicente's gang would listen to Bond or anyone and do an honest day's work. Nevertheless they managed in some miraculous way to be always in funds and to appear in the front rows at all cockfights, gambling on their favorites.

Tomas brought ugly stories of this group. He had a grapevine route of his own, and what he did not get in person was promptly relayed. Through Tomas I learned that their chief complaint was the separation of the sexes. Mean-while, in recognition of his excellent work as Chief, and his ability as a doctor, Dr. Dominguez had been transferred from Culion to Cebu, where he was to be director of the new leprosarium. To replace him, a Filipino physician had been sent down from Manila, a Dr. Demetrio Taborada. Soon after his arrival, Vicente and his followers presented a set of formal demands asking that there be more liberty between the sexes. There were a number of items, but the crux of the whole thing was that the young people wanted complete freedom to marry and have children.

Dr. Taborada was entirely powerless in this matter, which was subject to the decision based on the divergent viewpoints of the administration, medical science, religion and the individual. Such a decision must come from Manila. Permission to marry was given in only exceptional cases. Vicente understood little of this and laid at Dr. Taborada's door the failure to comply at once with the demands. Rumors were spreading that a revolt led by Vicente's gang was in prospect. We were all puzzled as to the form such a revolt would take, since the gang possessed no boats except a few rafts and bancas, and they would hardly carry anyone beyond the northern passage of Coron.

All this had been brewing for several weeks, when one night two messages came to me almost simultaneously. The first was the glad news that Dr. Bond and his wife were returning within a few days. The second was a sub-rosa message from Tomas that Vicente and his gang were actually on the warpath, and had decided to kill the Chief, and burn the doctors' houses in Balala.

There was no time to be lost. "Do you think the Chief knows of this, Tomas?"

"I do not know, sir. I saw him walking down the lower road and he looked very much unhappy. But maybe he knows—and maybe not."

"We must get to him at once. You must carry a note to him from me."

Tomas himself looked "very much unhappy" about that, so I told him not to bother. I would see to it myself. I did scribble a note to José Cruz instructing him to take parts out of our motors so that the boats could not be used, and sent Tomas off with that. Since I was going into Balala, I decided to walk. I armed myself with a heavy walking stick and went down through the colony toward the entrance to the upper level.

No patient was allowed to enter Balala except by special permission, and then it was usually for the lower road only. The new Administration Buildings had been built on that level, and sometimes we went down there. But rarely was a patient permitted to take this upper road which led to the doctors' homes. When I reached the gate dividing the two sections I saw the shallow wooden box containing a disinfectant into which the doctors and other well people stepped when leaving the colony. I hesitated, not knowing whether I should step in. Since I would not enter any house in Balala, I decided I had better not. I kept hoping that I would meet someone who would relieve me of my message, but as luck would have it the streets were empty and I came at last to the stone steps leading to the Chief's house. There I stood in the roadway and called to Dr. Taborada. His wife came out onto the lighted, wide bal-

cony running the full length of the single-storied house.
Seeing me she started, looked frightened, and ran back
into the house. In less than a minute her husband appeared and walked briskly down the stairs to where I was
waiting.

"Good evening, Mr. Ferguson. What is it?"

I told him quickly what I had learned.

"Perhaps, Doctor, you have already been warned."

"Good Heavens, no. It's a complete surprise. I had that
formal protest and sent it on to Manila. I had no idea they
would go this far. How did you learn about it?"

"Through Tomas. I do not know where he got his information, but I do know that it is usually correct."

"Thanks for coming. Whether this is true or false, we
will prepare. If there is further news, try to send it to me."

I promised, and retraced my steps.

It was long after that I got the full story of what happened in Balala that night. My message had an electric
effect. The Chief at once summoned all doctors and clerks
to his office in the Administration Building, to discuss what
plans could be made for protection. In the middle of the
meeting a lad came running in.

"They are going to kill the Chief and set fire to all
Balala!" he cried.

This was the last straw. The head clerk aroused a dozen
strong men as members of a hastily improvised civil guard.
There was a room in the back of the building where some
decrepit old Mausers donated to the colony by the constabulary were stored. Eager hands unlocked this room; the
ancient guns were dragged out. They were innocent of

bayonets and there was no ammunition. There followed a perfect tempest of action as the whole force searched feverishly for bullets. When a box of cartridges was finally found a loud "Hurrah!" rang out. They were also genuine antiques, and badly corroded. Some of the men fell to polishing them, so that they could be forced into the rifle barrels. A plan of defense was made and each man assigned to the spot he must guard.

These clerks of Balala were none too eager. In the first place they had very little confidence in the warning. But this was Balala, and the men who signed their pay vouchers were insisting on their services. They took the Mausers in their inexperienced hands and prepared to do or die. A few of the older men snapped the rifles open and inserted the shells, while the rest looked on open-eyed. Several of them stood holding the gun in one hand and the cartridges in the other, with no notion of how to get the two together. Finally each received a lesson in loading and taking aim.

"Take great care," warned the Chief. "When a patient approaches, challenge him and order him to return to the colony. If he continues to advance, stop him; if necessary, shoot."

Those who were assigned to posts along the two roads leading to the colony were in luck. They walked a hundred yards, stood in the shadow and watched. After a time they decided to sit, rather than stand guard, and from sitting it was not a great transition to recumbency and sweet slumber. The men assigned to the high ridge running back of Balala were not so fortunate. From the Administration Building, which was at sea level, it was a hard climb to the top of the hill. Those who made the top were winded, and dragged themselves wearily along to their posts. One of these recruits of the civil guard, exhausted by the climb, was struggling along the top of the ridge to his post of duty, dragging his rifle along with him, his fingers clutching the barrel, when the hammer caught on a twig, was jerked back and then released. There was a terrific explosion. The poor clerk made a wild leap into a thicket and ducked down, face buried in the heavy grass, waiting his doom. Fifty yards to his left another clerk, alarmed by the shot, started to run, and tripped over a root. His rifle went off and sent a screeching slug of lead tearing down the hill toward Balala. A stone tore a wide gash in his trousers as he fell, sprawling, on the hill's crest.

Meanwhile, below all was in turmoil. The roar of the first shot carried to every resident. The attack had begun! On the porch of one of the workingmen's houses on the outskirts of the community a crowd of terrified women and a few men had collected. At the sound, consternation was written on every face. A moment's silence—then the second rifle exploded. The bullet, descending, tore through the roof of the porch. Those present ducked as one person.

It was some time before they figured out that the shots had come from their own civil guard, and that they had been accidental. Indignation grew. The Chief ordered the civil guard back into camp. Runners started up the hill carrying his imperative command.

"Get those men and their guns back at once, but make them unload first!" It was long before Balala forgot the civil guard!

In the colony the drama enacted closely approached tragedy. While I had been taking the message to Dr. Taborada, and Tomas was away with his message to José Cruz, Carmen entered my house. She knew it well; she had often sewed for me. She went straight to my bedroom, took from its hiding place my army revolver, and with it concealed under her scarf slipped out of the house, down the road, and back to the colony. She went to the small place where Vicente and three other young men made their home, but no one was there. A boy on the road said that he had gone to the pier. She hurried there. I have always believed that Vicente had gone to look over our boats and that, had we taken no precautions, he and his gang would have made their getaway that night. As it was, Carmen came upon him examining a motor.

"Vicente!" she called. Instantly he raised up, pulling a small knife from his belt before he turned.

"Carmen? What the devil are you doing here?"

"I am here because I know what you wish to do. Don't give me talk. I know everything!"

"What are you talking about?"

"I know. Vicente, my brother, listen to me. You have seen how much your acts have displeased me; you know I have let you go your way. All my life, Vicente, I have protected you. Those nights on Mactan, how afraid I was to carry food and drink to you over the coral and up the hills! But I took them. Here in Culion, you have filled my heart with distress, with the way you have lived, and the things you have said. Still I held my peace. All this I have borne in my heart without reproach to you. But now! Now you are planning great evil. You would kill and burn; you would work your own ruin and mine. You would bring us to shame. I have accepted all the rest, this I will not." She drew the revolver from beneath her scarf and held it steady in her deformed hands. The barrel shone sinister through the dark. It was a punctuation mark no man could ignore.

"What in hell you trying to do?"

She stepped back and leveled the gun.

"Vicente, stop where you are! If you move toward me I pull the trigger. I have come to you to make you swear that you will stop this crazy plan to burn and kill. You will swear that you will stop or I swear by the love we bear our dead father that I shall kill you."

"Hell! Carmen, you wouldn't shoot your own brother."

She did not answer. The revolver was steady.

"You don't understand. Somebody's got to stop these jailers of ours, making us slaves, wanting us to work, shutting us up like criminals."

"Swear to me, Vicente."

"You wouldn't shoot your brother, Carmen. You couldn't do that."

"Swear, Vicente! Your time is short. Swear by our dead father who looks on us this night. If you break your oath and go one foot into Balala, I will hunt for you until I find you and kill you. Swear, swear!"

Vicente thought her mad. But she would do it, it was in her eyes. Hastily he mumbled, "By the love of our dead father, I swear. There, put away the gun."

She turned and fled. He stumbled after her but could not find her.

The mutineers did not attempt to carry out their plan to attack Balala, but that night Vicente and his gang raided one of the dormitories where the young girls lived and each lad carried off a girl. They fled to the hills and hid in the jungle. It was called The Lepers' Riot, and the newspapers of the world told of it in headlines.

Within three days the boat that carried Dr. and Mrs. Bond brought the constabulary. Despite the trouble we had been through, the entire colony, well and ill, everyone able to leave his bed, turned out to give Mrs. Bond a rousing welcome in recognition of her valiant work. Her boat was surrounded, a mile out, by an armada of leper's craft, carrying hundreds of our grateful community. Before then the couples had begun to creep in from the hills, driven back by hunger. The constabulary stayed a month, teaching the clerks at Balala how to use a rifle.

Vicente finally surrendered. As a menace to public peace he was put into jail and given an indeterminate sentence. A few of the ringleaders were sent away to another colony. Culion returned to its usual ways.

Tomas summed up the situation in a few words: "Many girls were seized and carried into the jungle. To carry a girl through the jungle is, I think, most difficult if it is against her will. This unwillingness could have been overcome only with co-operation, I think."

VISITORS' DAY, AND THE BOAT WAS COMING in! I always avoided these visits of families and relatives of the patients. When I was new to the colony I had attended once. To see what happened then was enough for a lifetime. Mothers came to see—and not touch—their children. Wives came to see, and talk with—and no more—their stricken husbands. Homesick boys and girls came to stare at fathers and mothers who might never again hold them in their arms. Sometimes frantic visitors or patients broke loose to enfold relatives in close embrace. They were forcibly disengaged by doctors, nurses or the leper police. I had grown hardened to my own illness and to my fate. But I never could accustom myself to the fate of all these others, particularly the children. It made me fairly sick to watch, and I stayed away.

When a visitors' boat was expected, all business was abandoned. Patients could not be expected to work. If no one of their own family or friends were coming, they hung about listening to the latest news from the home barrio, suffering vicariously with those who met their loved ones.

Tomas left to meet the boat although he expected no one as far as I knew. I got out my old phonograph. I had not played it for months, and I began running all my records. Out of another world came the music of that song Jane had written, "our song." It sent me across the Pacific; where had life taken Jane? As it finished I heard my name called and went to the porch. Carita stood below, smiling up at me. I leaped the steps, put out my hand and jerked it back. Carita was no longer one of us. I dared not touch her.

"Don't be silly, Ned." She stepped up to bring her face level with mine, put her arms about me, and kissed me.

"There is no fear between us, nor will there ever be."

"Carita, I had no idea you were coming. I would have come to the boat to meet you."

"I didn't want you to know. I planned a surprise. It has been nice, hasn't it?"

" 'Nice' isn't the word! How are you? Come along to our old spot under the mangoes."

"Ned, darling, how wonderful the place looks! You never neglect anything. Dear, you were right. My family took me back without fear. Others avoided me at first. But I have been extremely fortunate. Dr. Bond and Dr. Dominguez have helped me. I asked them not to tell you. I am working with the Board of Health. My task is to check on patients who have been paroled. It is not easy to trace some when they leave their own barrios. If they have been neglectful, I persuade them to continue re-examinations at regular intervals, also to take such treatment as the doctors think necessary. They trust me, since I have been one of them. Some of those who are paroled become positive again, and must be induced to return here or to go to Cebu. That is the sad part of our work. Dr. Bond is right when he says we must find out how to prevent this disease; that is the one thing that matters for all time."

"Do you think those of the outside world will recover from their fear of lepers returned as negatives?"

"Yes, certainly, someday when the cause and cure of leprosy are understood. My experiences since I have been working with the paroles have convinced me that one of the most important steps which could be taken in the fight against leprosy would be to find a new word with which to describe it, just as was the case with tuberculosis. The terrifying word 'consumptive' had to be changed before people could look sanely on that illness, whether they were its victims or its spectators. The same thing is true of leprosy, only in an exaggerated degree. The word 'leper' has come to mean much more than a person suffering from a particular illness; an illness which you and I know is often not disfiguring and which probably could not be transmitted to a well person, even if the infected one were bent on doing so.

"The word 'leper' has wound its way into the literature of the world, to describe not a disease, not a sick person, but a moral pariah, a vile person who deserves nothing from his fellows because of his vileness.

"Ned, they have branded you and me with a term like that! They have branded these children, these babies running about the streets of Culion with a term like that!

"We need the help of the doctors. We need those who

will work at this problem until they finally release mankind from its curse, but more than anything, it seems to me, my darling, we need that the world shall cease to call us lepers."

She was crying. I had seen Carita through difficult times, personal problems. I was abashed before this torrent of emotions which was in no sense personal, or was it?

When she was calm she went on. "I am glad that I am doing this work for those who are paroled—I wanted to come back to tell you that. And there is another reason for my visit. Carmen is here."

"I'll say she is. Why didn't you write to me, Carita? What is Carmen doing back here anyhow? Dr. Ponce says she is still negative—why—"

"Hold your horses, is not that your quaint saying, Ned? I have already heard that Carmen has become a heroine in Culion. Perhaps that is a good omen for her future. She is here for a very important reason."

"Carmen must be crazy. She has been cured. Why in God's name should she come back to this place?"

Carita's musical laugh stopped me.

"Ned, you are a dear. But oh, you are a stupid! Are you really so dense? Don't you know that Carmen and Tomas are much in love?"

She had me there. Carmen had visited my house often. Dumbbell that I was not to have seen. But I was stubborn.

"Even so, why should Carmen come back here?"

"She has returned to marry Tomas, even though they may not live together, since she is a parole."

"What kind of a marriage will that be, Carita? Why do they marry if they must be separated?"

"Have a little patience, Ned. There are so many sides to

this story. Tomas and Carmen know, and will respect the ruling. But they prefer to marry anyhow. Carmen has been away for some time. There is no one left of her family but one younger brother. Father and mother are both dead. The brother is living with an uncle and aunt, and all three fear any contact with her. Carmen has been staying with me. Her embroidery is beautiful but with her crippled hands she cannot work fast enough to make a living. She has been eating her heart out with homesickness for Tomas and her one consolation has been visiting with Tomas's mother, who is now old. After their marriage Carmen will go back to live with Mrs. Aguilar and to help care for her. Tomas will be able to assist them."

For a little I sat mulling it over. Carita was silent. I thought I knew all the tragedies that could befall a leper, but here was a kind new to me. Tomas, my son—

"Carmen will find some happiness in waiting for Tomas and in taking care of his mother, Ned."

"Waiting for Tomas? He has been here nearly twenty years. How can Carmen be so foolish as to think that he will ever leave?"

"She has talked with the doctors. You saw her, I believe, with Dr. Ponce. All the doctors have been kind. She understands that Tomas is one of the baffling cases, where the disease seems not to progress, and yet when tests are made the return is always positive. She has more faith in the future than the doctors themselves. She is wildly happy. A ceremony is the most the law will permit—and Tomas and Carmen love each other enough to want to belong to each other legally, since they may have nothing more. Carmen, at least, believes without doubt that some day Tomas will come to her. You know, Ned, Carmen has been cured. No one here ever stops hoping, and her hope for herself has been justified."

I looked down. There was my signature on the table top, a signature twelve years old. It marked my armistice with hope. God bless them if they could still hope.

Patiently Carita waited. It seemed a long time before I could pull myself together.

"Well, Carita, may I be permitted to see the culprits and to give them my blessing? I've no doubt you have them hidden somewhere about."

"You are becoming quite clever, Ned." She went to the edge of the porch and called. Instantly Tomas and Carmen appeared.

"Señora Torres has given me to understand that you and Carmen wish to marry and that she has come back for the ceremony."

I turned to Carmen. How little she was, this brave young woman! I looked down at the bouquet of flowers she held to conceal what remained of her hands.

"Carmen, my child, I bid you welcome. Now, Carita, I know that you have it all planned. Tell me about the wedding."

"On Rizal Day, Ned. And I shall stay over for it, you may be sure."

"That is the best news of all, eh, Tomas?"

"We-ll, sir, Señora Torres is, after you, sir, our best friend."

And so it was settled.

With preparations for the wedding going on, my

thoughts were much on Tomas. I knew that the doctors were doing all that could be done, but I was not satisfied. I managed to have a long talk with Dr. Taborada.

"Tomas came here with me, Doctor. Apparently he has not changed at all. There are few signs of the disease on his body and they were there when he came. Yet the report always comes that his reaction to tests is positive."

"There are others here like him. It sometimes happens that a patient will remain that way all his life. One like Tomas could walk the streets of Manila and no one would suspect that he was not a well man. Yet the bacilli are in his body and so he may be even a greater menace, since he would not be shunned as would a patient who bore upon face and hands the marks of the disease. Sometimes I think that those like Tomas, and those who are dismissed as negative but who cannot make a living because people still fear them, are as much to be pitied as those who are actually pronounced heavy cases. There was an old man in a leprosarium near Surabaya, Java, when I last visited there. Few signs of the disease were upon him and yet he had been in that place as a positive for forty years."

Forty years! I thought of my signature on the table top. It was well that I had signed an armistice with hope. But Tomas still hoped.

When I got home I went down to the beach and tried to think out a future for Tomas. While I remained at Culion he would be looked after. He had continued his studies and recently had added to his duties some special work in book-keeping and accounting for me, for which I paid him extra. In marrying he would assume responsibility for Carmen, and for some time he had been sending money to his mother. It might be possible to train him so that he could eventually have a place in the business.

We were in the middle of another expansion of our business. With new equipment and an augmented force we could produce enough power to enable consumers to install refrigerators. Americans, hungry for ice, iced dishes and iced drinks, were good customers. Most of the Filipino doctors and administration employees had learned to use ice. But the patients cared little for it, had they been able to pay for it. They all joined in a desire for radios though, now that current was available, and those who were able purchased cheap sets.

Tomas had accepted the choice of Rizal Day as a happy omen. In reality the commemoration is of a day of sadness, since on that day José Rizal was executed. Rizal is one of the great men of all time. Executed at thirty-five, his brief life has left an ineffaceable impression upon his countrymen. A man with as many talents as Leonardo da Vinci or Benjamin Franklin, he was first a patriot, a patriot who never led a revolt although he was twice jailed and finally shot by the Spaniards on charges of sedition, trumped-up charges without a word of truth in them.

Rizal was both a poet and an historian. His book *Noli Me Tangere* caricatured the Spaniards, and was the indirect cause of his death. But aside from his political convictions— he was in reality a democrat—Rizal in his brief life won recognition in many fields. Throughout Europe he was recognized as one of the greatest oculists of his day. He was a sculptor, and an ethnologist; his collections are preserved in the Dresden Museum. He was a zoologist and an accomplished linguist, able to write in a dozen languages, as well as a portraitist and caricaturist. He wrote novels, poignant and powerful, which attracted attention far beyond the Philippines. He was an educator and an able civil engineer. Exiled in Mindanao, in one small town he established a new kind of school and then built the town waterworks! When yellow fever broke out in Cuba he volunteered from exile to serve in a hospital as an interne, and was released and sent. It was while on his way to Cuba, via Barcelona, that he was taken from the ship and again jailed. Returned to Manila, he was put into solitary confinement at Fort Santiago and after seven weeks of imprisonment was tried, with no choice of a lawyer, and condemned.

Throughout the Islands he is known as the "George Washington of the Philippines." For his memory Tomas had a reverence amounting to adoration. To be married on Rizal Day was therefore a double consummation.

The day before the wedding the men from the plant and the fishing business sent José Cruz to me.

"If you will consent, Mr. Ned," said José, "we have decided to vote to Tomas Aguilar a few shares in the stock of the company as a wedding gift."

It pleased Tomas immensely. It helped him to feel that, along with acquiring a wife, he was gaining a status in the community. A good Number One house boy in the Philippines has a position of responsibility and importance which scarcely has a counterpart in occidental civilization. He is a kind of combination butler, chef, secretary and confidential aid, and as such has social standing. Tomas, however, deserved a wider recognition and this stock was the beginning of a new life for him.

The ceremony was performed at noon, under the mangoes, and it seemed to me that half the colony attended. There were a number of special guests; about twenty girls from the dormitory where Carmen had lived, and a number of Carita's friends. Tomas had invited the young men of an athletic club to which he belonged.

Father Marello in his white robes was everywhere, laughing, cracking jokes at the expense of the bride and groom. And Mr. Manson made a good second, although he was newer to the colony and his flock a much smaller one.

The most uncomfortable guest was the Officiating Chief, Dr. Taborada, who had been asked to perform the wedding ceremony since Carmen and Tomas belonged to different faiths. It was an unusual job for him and naturally he was suffering stage fright. I had seen him in the operating room of the hospital getting ready to amputate a leg and he was as cool as a surgeon should be. Marrying Tomas and Carmen was a far more difficult job, and he trembled in body and voice as he read the brief lines. The watching crowd sensed this and grew very still. The wave of sympathy from the hushed audience reached Taborada. His voice grew steadier and at the close he was quite himself. Then the wedding procession and invited guests, led by the bride in her exquisite gown and Tomas with his head held higher than I had ever seen it, walked slowly and with dignity down to the long tables placed on the beach. Here was served the famous lechon, a dish without which no wedding in the Philippines could ever be complete, delectable beyond the ability of the uninitiate to imagine! Fish, boiled and roasted, rice and many sweet pastries which are the Filipinos' special delight; coconut ice cream, native fruits, and oranges and apples, a special treat. Many of those present had never seen apples before.

Our well guests had a special table, and their food was supplied from Balala. Their house boys waited upon them.

Shag and Mame did well at this party. They circulated among the tables and reaped so many choice tidbits that I was forced to have them shut up for the remainder of the time. The dogs were getting along in years. The heat of the tropics was telling on them, and overfeeding was not good.

The uninvited guests, as well as the others, roundly applauded all the speeches. Called upon, I could not well refuse, so I rose to say,

"God bless you, my children," and sat down again. I never was a speech maker.

The sounds of stringed music came floating down to us. It was our Number One orchestra—which had come to honor the bride and groom. José Cruz clapped for attention.

"We are going to have a wedding dance. Tomas, you and Carmen must lead in the grand march."

The younger people paired off and paraded around the grounds several times. Then they lined up on four sides facing each other, and began the intricate figures of the stately rigadon. It was a beautiful thing to watch as the dancers moved back and forth and wound in and out. Dressed in their dainty piña frocks of pastel hues, the girls looked like multi-colored butterflies. The men wore the usual white trousers with transparent shirts.

Laboratory and bridge leading to the new research wards.

New Leonard Wood Memorial Laboratory at Culion.

(top) The Leonard Wood Monument, showing the long steps to Rizal Plaza in the background. This monument was designed and built by the patients.

(bottom) The square in front of Colony Hall, showing the Leonard Wood Monument and the stone steps to Rizal Plaza.

After an hour of dancing, a gaily decorated truck drew up at the gate. Carmen was assisted to a high box seat, which was decked with flowers and bunting, and Tomas, with much merriment, was placed on a low wooden box at her feet.

Then the procession began. Behind the truck the girls and lads fell in, two by two. After them came the other guests, and at the last, the gate crashers.

Carita and I stayed to say good-by to the older people who did not intend to join the procession. Finally we were alone.

"That was terribly nice of you, Ned, to call them your children."

"They are my children. If I ever leave this place I shall provide for them. Let's take the car down to the theater. You must be weary."

We drove slowly, turned off the road into the open space that led to the Plaza, and stopped before the monument erected to Leonard Wood.

"I have a special pride in this, Carita. It was conceived and executed by the colonists themselves, and it was dedicated only a short time ago. It is really a good likeness of Wood."

"Your boyhood hero," she said softly.

It was but a short distance to the theater. The wedding party had not yet arrived.

In my years on Culion I had been surfeited with speeches, but the speech of that day I wanted to hear. Francisco Bonifacio, President of the Leper Council and Principal of Schools, was the orator. It was rumored that he was a distant relative of the famous Bonifacio, the Philippine patriot, who had organized the Katipunan, the revolutionary organization which started the Insurrection against the Spanish régime.

He was about forty, slender and lithe, with a heavy shock of coal-black hair and a thin, almost aesthetic face in which glowed keen, black eyes. He had considerable influence in the colony and had never given any indication of radical leanings. But throughout the Islands there was increasing and constant agitation for independence. It seemed an excellent time for Bonifacio as one of the most intelligent members of the colony to speak his mind.

Soon the theater was full and people were standing all about. Through the crowd the wedding party moved slowly and triumphantly down the aisle, Carmen and Tomas leading. The girl looked wonderful; her eyes sparkled and her whole face glowed in this, her hour. It seemed a queer celebration for a wedding party to come to hear a political speech. Queer, that is, to an American. To the Filipinos it was perfectly fitting. We rose as Mr. Manson gave the invocation, after which the entertainment began—recitations and songs by various members of the colony. Then Dr. Taborada made a brief speech and introduced Bonifacio.

His predecessor had always begun public speeches with the lugubrious salutation: "My fellow unfortunates . . ." Bonifacio walked to the front of the platform amid generous applause, and held up his hand for silence.

"Citizens of Culion—" There was a stir all along the rows. In those three words he had managed to put all of us on a plane of dignity. Lepers we were, but we were also citizens, not criminals deprived of our right to vote, but citizens.

He went briefly through the story of José Rizal, following to the execution:

"By that volley a lone man, martyr and hero, calm and unblindfolded, fell. That man had never urged separation from Spain by violence. He personally had been the recipient of the old world's culture and learning. He sought for his people both the blessings of that culture and the national stature which would come only through freedom. Rizal probably never dreamed of the unexpected source from which that freedom was to come. Sixteen months later the fleet of a powerful country from across the Pacific, steamed into Manila Bay, engaged the Spanish fleet in battle, and completely destroyed it. Three months after that the American flag was flying over the city of Manila. Today there fly all over the Islands, these two flags." He pointed to the Stars and Stripes, with the Philippine flag just beneath it, three yellow stars and a yellow sunburst on white, above two panels, one red and one blue. There was a burst of applause.

"It is unfortunate that there should be among us a few who seem blind to the blessings they are even now enjoying. Those things for which our great hero Rizal pleaded, worked and died, are being done this day, here, by our own people. It is true that we are taught and aided by Americans. Is it significant?

"I want independence for my country. I also want freedom, freedom from ignorance, disease and poverty. Man has not yet accomplished all of these in any country. But in thirty years we of these Islands have made strides that have taken other nations centuries. I know! As a school teacher I have watched the rise of school buildings—the

arch enemies of ignorance—in every province of the Islands. Our children march each day to these buildings to
secure arms against this foe. We have all seen the constant
advance of law and order. We have seen more. Our own
people steadily replace those of our foster country, as soldiers, policemen, officers of law and justice. The Chief of
this Colony today is a Filipino, Dr. Demetrio Taborada.

"We have seen more. The roads, which were carabao
tracks, stretch for hundreds of kilometers, so that we may
travel in safety, on hard paving. Our people have grown
more prosperous; they have more food, more clothing and
more amusement. Above all, we citizens of Culion know,
day by day and hour by hour, how disease is being conquered. Cholera, smallpox, malaria are well under control.
We live longer. The mortality rate during the years since
the Americans came has been reduced. In 1898, the last
years of the Spanish régime, the death rate was 30.5 per
thousand population; in 1929 it was 21.7. That means a
saving of more than eighty thousand lives in a single year.

"And we who are lepers"—as Bonifacio said it, the word
was an accolade of distinction·-"we, who fight day after
day that mysterious enemy which has challenged mankind
almost from the beginning of recorded time, we know that
within the past few years the star of hope has risen for us.
We have seen men and women leave this place, never to
return. For them, the enemy is conquered; they have been
restored to the world.

"When we are ready for independence, it will be ours.
We are learning to use knowledge, and order, and health,
and in this we are aided by hands extended across the seas.

"The Philippines gave to the world in José Rizal, a man

worthy to stand among the great in history. In science, in art, he is known and acknowledged as a leader, both in Europe and in America. We can never forget that it was the first American Governor-General, William Howard Taft, who set apart this day, which we are now commemorating, as our national holiday.

"On a day to come, a single flag will fly over these Islands. By that time there may be many of those who are now present who, with restored health, will be free to go wherever their hearts desire. When that day comes, we shall still remember!"

I stole a glance along the row of faces. Carmen and Tomas, looking upward with liquid eyes. Upon Carita's face an exaltation I had seen on that of Sister Victoire.

Bonifacio was reading Rizal's last poem, written in his cell as he awaited dawn, and the firing squad.

Farewell dear Fatherland, clime of the sun caressed,
Pearl of the Orient seas, our Eden lost;
Gladly I go to give thee this faded life's best
And were it brighter, fresher, or more blest
Still would I give it thee, nor count the cost.

When even my grave is remembered no more,
Unmarked by never a cross or stone,
Let the plough sweep through it; the spade turn it o'er
That my ashes may carpet thine earthly floor,
Before into nothingness they are blown.

Farewell to you all, from my soul torn away,
Friends of my childhood in the home dispossessed
Give thanks that I rest from the wearisome day!
Farewell to thee too, sweet friend that lightened my way,
Beloved creatures all, farewell! In death there is rest!

CHAPTER ꜰ ꜰ ꜰ ꜰ ꜰ ꜰ ꜰ ꜰ ꜰ ꜰ THIRTY

In the evening Tomas and Carmen went off to see the motion pictures. Culion had again witnessed the "helping hand from across the seas." With the coming of sound films in the United States there was a great accumulation of silent films on the shelves, unused. The motion picture companies of America had sent to us as a gift great quantities selected from these pictures, and they were shown twice a week.

Carita and I stayed at home. Her boat was due the next day. Carmen would go with her. Both of us knew we might not meet again for a long, long time. We sat on the porch lingering over our coffee, and cakes which Carita had made. I noticed that clouds had begun to roll up in the east over Coron. A sharp breeze was blowing and it was evident that rain was on the way. Above our voices we could hear the sighing of the reefs. It was a curious phenomenon, that wail of the reefs. Before a storm, they could always be heard lamenting. Suddenly Shag threw back his head and howled. From the beach Mame responded. Carita was puzzled.

"I never knew them to do that, Ned."

"You would think a 'baguio' was on its way. But a typhoon is unlikely so late in the year."

Someone was coming around the porch. It was a clerk from the Chief's office looking for Carita.

"We have a message, Señora Torres. The *Gravina* will not arrive tomorrow. There is a typhoon and she is remaining at Puerto Princessa or at Cuyo. You will be informed when she is expected."

"Hurrah for the baguio! Carita, this means you will be here another day, perhaps several days longer. Good news for me!"

"I hope it will not harm this wonderful place of yours, Ned."

She was anxiously looking out to sea.

José Cruz was at the foot of the steps.

"Pardon, Señora Torres. But, Ned, they say a baguio is coming. How about the boats?"

"Get some of the men and see that the boats are anchored out in the bay. Why, Tomas!" For he and Carmen, breathless, stood by José.

"Yes, sir. They told us at the theater that a typhoon was coming and all left to prepare. Number six signal is now up."

"Number six! Carita, I have not seen that signal since I've been here. This must be the real thing and it's headed our way."

Even as I spoke, a squall passed over the Island. José,

Tomas and Carmen jumped up to the shelter of the porch. Sudden lightning illuminated the house, grounds and bay.

"Ned, you must go with José. Tomas, Carmen and I will stay here and make the house secure."

"But they don't really need me."

"Yes, they do, Ned. Ask José."

"The men will be much excited. It is better that you come."

"Okay, José. Tomas, drag in the poles in the yard and brace them against the west side. See that they are raised and made firm. Put in the braces for the windows on the porch."

"Carmen is strong; she will help too." Tomas was proudly recommending his bride. I snatched up a light raincoat and went down the road. It was empty. As we passed the first house we saw the entire family out struggling with long bamboo poles. These fragile nipa houses could stand an amazing amount of wind if properly braced. The other houses were being braced in like fashion. The storekeepers were letting down shutters and piling their small stocks in the center of the rooms. When we reached the beach leading to our piers I could see the colony lights going out one by one. That meant shutters going down. The hospital windows, tall and broad, were blotted out one after another. The sea was already wild and the wind so strong that we had hard work against it. Rain squalls drenched us. The two large motor boats were anchored at some distance from shore and were heaving at their lines. At the pier were a number of smaller boats, outrigger bancas and smaller motors. Ricardo Jacildo and Victor Cabisan had already arrived and were working like mad. I sent Victor off to bring all hands and to leave word at the plant that the entire crew should turn out to protect it. José, Jacildo and I took a small skiff and went out to one of the big fishing boats. We got her moving and out halfway into the bay. Then we dropped the heavy anchor, seldom used, but kept for emergencies. We had a tough tussle getting back into our small boat. But we made it.

By the time we were back at the pier once more there were a dozen hands to help. I set them to work pulling the outriggers up on the beach. These were followed by the rafts and small motor boats. Then we went out again to take the second big boat to deeper anchorage. The wind and rain subsided and gave us a breathing space and we made good time. The lightning confused us; the whole sky would suddenly blaze and drive us blind. We had just got her anchored when there was great shouting from the pier. One of our bancas was out, riding away from land at terrific speed. With the next flood of light we could see a figure in the stern, swinging to the tiller, a bad spot in such a sea as this. The waves would break over the bow and smother man and boat; then they rode clear again. We neared the pier and could hear words.

"Vicente, it's Vicente! He broke jail! Stop him!"

No one could stop that madman. I shouted to him but the wind drowned my voice. He yelled back and waved an upflung arm. The banca with that upright figure in the stern passed out of the inner harbor and out of sight. He might make Coron—but it was a long chance.

I struggled back to the house alone, fighting the wind and rain. Carita, Tomas and Carmen had done everything possible to protect the place. Carita, bless her, had even had Tomas carry poles to brace my beloved flame tree.

"Carita, there will be few people on the Island who will sleep tonight. You and Carmen will be safer here than anywhere; this house is better built than most of them. I will take the responsibility if any fault is found. Besides"—I smiled down at her—"you see I just like to have you around. I ordered this baguio just to keep you."

We stayed on the porch through it all, keeping a single window unshuttered as long as we could. We could see the play of lightning over the islands, catch glimpses of huge, white-crested waves piling in, see the coconut palms bending their tufted heads to the fury of the wind. Toward morning the blow became more and more intense. Rain was driven clear across the length of the porch and a banana tree crashed, falling against the wall of the house. I closed the last shutter. The electric lights had failed us early in the evening, and there was only the faint glow of a hurricane lantern I had hung in one corner of the porch.

Shag and Mame were with us. They had stopped howling, but they were restless and if we moved, rose and followed us about. The storm seemed to rouse Carita. She was fearlessly gay, and the intoxication of the baguio finally got through to me. After several hours of noise there came a dead calm. We knew that we were in the very center of the typhoon. I opened the shutters. The rain had ceased; the wind had gone. Tomas and I went out to see that our braces were holding. Shortly we would be struck from the opposite side, as this revolving torrent of demoniacal wind passed over us. We moved some of the braces, facing them in reverse to meet the final act. The lightning showed my yard full of debris; the fence had been torn down by trees

crashing through. Huge branches had been broken off the
mangoes and we stumbled over coconuts everywhere.
Scarcely had we returned to the porch when the howl of
the wind was again about us. We sat out what remained
of the night. There was too much noise for talking; we
exchanged but brief words. Shag and Mame snuggled close
to us.

In the morning the rain stopped. We went out and to
our joy found that the real damage was slight. Patches were
loose on the roof, some parts had actually been torn off,
and in one or two places panels of swali in the sides of the
house were missing. The coconut trees had been hit hardest. Several of them stood bare, topless, looking like electric
light poles. The beach and yard were littered with all kinds
of wreckage, leaves, branches, coconuts, timber. A part of
a rowboat was in the middle of my front lawn. I examined
it; it was not mine.

We walked slowly through the colony. In some places
the damage was greater than at my house. But on the whole
Culion had come through pretty well. No one had been
killed; one patient had suffered rather severe injury when
the side of his house came down upon him. That same
morning Carmen heard of Vicente's escape. She took it very
quietly. I knew she realized he could not have ridden out
the typhoon. No one else mourned. His little group dis-
solved. The double warning of the failure of the uprising
with the jailing of their leader, and the baguio, was too
much for them.

On the second day after the typhoon the *Gravina* came.
The Chief gave Tomas and me special permission to go to

the Balala pier to see Carita and Carmen off. They were there when we arrived.

Parting from Carita was agony for me and I could guess by the distress in her eyes that it was no less hard for her. She stood on the deck, waving, until the steamer had passed from sight. A few days later she wrote that she was being sent to Mindanao to work in the interior, far from Manila and farther still from Culion. With that letter I had a feeling that I would not see her again.

CHAPTER ✦ ✦ ✦ ✦ ✦ ✦ ✦ ✦ THIRTY-ONE

WALTER SIMPSON WAS LEAVING US. HE HAD been in bad health for several years; nephritis had him, as it had so many of our fellow patients. He kept on working and I admired his grit. An epidemic of encephalitis—brain fever—broke out in Manila and for some unknown reason a few cases developed in Culion. Simpson was one of them. He asked to be removed to San Lazaro. He knew a doctor, a man in the Army Medical Corps, in whom he had great faith. Walter was well able to pay for the trip and permission came promptly. He was three months at San Lazaro, but the disease was too much for him. He died there.

It was up to me to do two things: to fill in Simpson's place for a time and to train my men so that the plant and fishing business would go on without him and eventually without me. I thought a long time before I called a meeting. When the men did report I found they had been thinking about this for some time.

That was an eye-opener for me. I must appear feebler than I had thought. . . . We voted that José Cruz should succeed Walter, with Victor Cabisan as his assistant. These men proved entirely satisfactory both to me and to the other stockholders. In my particular work, the accounting and financial end, Tomas was recognized as my official assistant.

Shortly after this meeting I received a message that Dr. Bond wanted to see me at the clinic. I was surprised since I had received my regular treatment and examination only the day before.

I went down to see him immediately.

"Ned," he said, "I looked over your card this morning. I'm sorry to tell you that your heart is not behaving as it should."

"Give me the low-down, Jack. I want the truth. Is it pretty bad?"

"It's none too good, old fellow. A moderate amount of work won't hurt you, but you must not tire yourself."

"And hunting?"

"That's out."

"Looks as if you're retiring me from active duty."

"Not exactly, only you must be careful."

He walked with me to the door. "Have you heard that the President of the United States has called in all gold?"

"No, I haven't. Does that apply to us?"

"Yes, an inspector is coming down from Manila."

When the inspector came I ran the car down to Colony Hall to watch the returns. The doctors had made it possible to avoid contact with the patients by pulling a long table across an open doorway. The inspector sat on the inner side. The pieces were dropped into a disinfectant and the inspector wore gloves. The colony coins had been thoroughly disinfected. When I arrived, the inspector, a young man in uniform who wore thick spectacles, was already busy. Piled on the table were gold pieces, cherished gold pieces which had been polished to a luster rivaling the sunshine. There were many curious pieces, coins unknown in America; the inspector had a hard time of it. Using a glass he examined Spanish doubloons, Asiatic pieces, rough pieces from little-known islands. Some of the coins looked hand-minted.

He would take them in the forceps, use his supplementary glasses, weigh them, consult various books he had with him, and shake a doubtful head. Finally he had to make a decision. His confidence grew as the day passed. Not a patient questioned his award. They left, with contentment on their faces, carrying the colony money which they had received.

But it was not only coins the inspector was called upon to appraise. The President of the United States had called for gold. From my chair placed near the doorway but in the shadow, I saw Jacildo step before the table. Proudly he laid down a gold eagle, U.S.A., and a small gold piece (worth two and a half American dollars) with a hole pierced through, such a coin as a baby might wear on a chain about its neck. He was followed by Marcia, the daughter of one of my men, and one whom I had always thought a very frivolous young woman. Her face alight, Marcia took from her ears, from her neck, hands and arms, earrings, chains, bracelets.

"Before I came here," she said, "I was to have married. My intended husband gave these to me. Is it enough?"

The inspector protested.

"It is not necessary that you should bring jewelry. Of course if you wish to turn it in, we are very glad to receive it."

"I wish," said Marcia with great firmness. "It is true that I like jewelry. It is also true that my father and I have found help and happiness in this Island. If the United States needs gold we wish to send it."

The inspector coughed. "By all means." He made ready to pay in colony coinage. Tomas, who was next in line, laid his possessions on the table.

A battered locket, sent to Tomas by his adored mother. The locket had at one time contained the pictures of both father and mother. Now it was empty. Somewhere Tomas cherished the pictures. Five shining, bright eagles, fifty dollars.

The inspector's eyes clouded.

"And where did these come from?"

"Mr. Peter Brant, of Manila, sent them to me as wedding gift. Mr. Brant is a friend of Mr. Ned Ferguson, who sits here by the doorway. I am Mr. Ferguson's Number One boy."

"It is quite all right, inspector," I assured him. "Mr. Brant sent the eagles by Señora Carita Torres."

"Thank you, Mr. Ferguson. Well, young man, you have quite a bit of value here." Tomas left, his eyes shining.

They came and came—mothers with their children's trinkets, young men and women with coins and finery. There was a lump in my throat as I, an American, watched.

I was very humble as I laid down my little pile. I had not thought of jewelry, but I added my watch. I had another at home anyhow; this had been dad's. He would have wished it. I took up my pile of colony coins.

"When it is all over, inspector, will you do me a favor? I would like to know what it all amounts to."

"Tomorrow afternoon I shall be able to tell you. Of course you may know, Mr. Ferguson."

I came back the next day with a couple of pairs of cuff links and some gold shirt studs. I sat waiting, until I was the last. As I took my coins, he smiled.

"There is a total of six thousand pesos, and perhaps a few additional."

Three thousand dollars!

That gold went down to the Treasury Department in Washington, D. C., from the lepers of Culion.

Dr. Ravino, who had been my guide to San Lazaro, came to Culion the next year. Time had dealt lightly with him. He was stouter, a little bald, but his energy was that of a young man. He came to see me shortly after his arrival. His friendship was a boon to me, for despite all that he and Jack Bond could do I was slipping rapidly downhill. The dream that had lived with me, was ended. That dream, which had beset me day and night ever since years before, when I sat in a railroad train and stared out at my home city slipping away from me, the dream that one day I would return home cured, restored in my right to touch any man and not harm him, the right to mingle with my kind without fear, without shame—that dream was over. I had been a leper for nearly a quarter century.

Many nights I sat on the porch alone. No not alone. For Shag and Mame who had grown old with me, were my constant companions. As I stared out over the shining waters I went over my life bit by bit. I had fought my own fight in this place of isolation. In the eyes of men here, in the eyes of men anywhere, I had not been too unsuccessful as far as material achievement went. My share in the plants, and my cash, amounted to forty thousand pesos. I did not actually own the land on which the house stood; the government owned it, but the house was mine. Twenty thousand dollars and a home.

In my town in the States a man who with little aid had lived his life and accumulated a house and twenty thousand dollars would not be considered a failure. In the community in which I lived I was accepted not only as a member, but as a person of some prestige. True, it was a community of lepers, and because it was such a community, it held certain unique values. The normal human being has certain necessities placed upon him by his environment. Here we were freed from all necessities save one which we shared with all others, to keep up the good fight, whatever it happened to be. But in our community there was no point in any man's pretending to be other than he was. He need not think anything but that which he wanted to think. As a leper he was dependent; but as a leper he had a curious and very real independence unknown to normal men. I took my acceptance in the community to mean that my neighbors held my actions and thinking worthy of their respect, and that they had given that respect to me.

All this I had achieved. I had built for myself in my home the beauty so essential to the very existence of the spirit. This home which I loved and enjoyed, and which my friends enjoyed, could be mine to the end. I could die here, and living or dead be with friends.

One night it came to me without warning and in full tide that I did not want to remain longer. I was sick, old, tired. I wanted, more than I had ever wanted anything, home. I wanted to see the sun rising over the plains. I wanted to see the cattle grazing on the hillsides. I wanted to see the maples growing in the grove just beyond a white farmhouse. I wanted to see clean white roads leading God knows where. I wanted the smoke of factories and red-bricked stores crowding each other along Main Street. I wanted America. I wanted to see about me my own kind, my own countrymen. There were rumors that the Stars and Stripes were coming down out here. That ere long the army would go home, the navy would go home. I wanted terribly to go home, too.

At the first opportunity I told Bond of what I'd been thinking.

"I understand, Ned. Is there anything I can do to help you?"

"Yes, if you would write to Winton about arranging my transfer to Carville."

"Of course I will. I'll get a letter off at once."

It was some months before the reply came. Bond brought me the word. "Winton has taken the matter up with the United States Public Health Service and the War Department. Everything is arranged. You are to go to Manila and there take an army transport to San Francisco. From there by train to Carville. The transport will sail on the fifteenth of next month.

"I am sorry that I shall not be here to see you off but I'm leaving on the mail boat in the morning to attend a conference in India."

He remained several hours. We talked of many things we had shared. When it came to the leave-taking we were too moved to prolong it.

"Good-by, Jack."

"Good-by, Ned. Good luck."

I was not too old or too tired or too ill to escape the stimulus of Winton's letter. It fired my spirit and my body to new enthusiasm. My country was taking me back; the army was taking me back, under its own protection. I was to be repatriated; I was going home!

CHAPTER THIRTY-TWO

At noon I was to board the little inter-island boat that was to start me on the long journey home. I had not slept much the night before. Through the long hours I lay there, listening to the tinkling music. There was a moon and, as usual, the songs went on until its setting. Shag and Mame moved restlessly from yard to house, from house to yard. Once Shag came and stood for a long time by my bed, staring at me through the mosquito netting. Could they know, these two animals who had been my faithful companions for so long? Both of them were old and Mame was sick, almost finished with life. It had taken me a long time to decide what to do. Dr. Ravino helped me out. Mame could not live much longer. Shag, her mate of years, would not long survive her. Before I left, I would put them to sleep—but it was going to be a heartbreaking ordeal.

On the porch Tomas was setting the table for breakfast,

moving swiftly, softly and silently. I could see him stealing quick glances at me, and his eyes were liquid with moisture. His hands shook as he placed the blue plates on the table. In a bowl was a cluster of blue orchids.

"Breakfast, sir." His voice was husky. I played with the golden mango, glistening with cold. He had put before me all my favorite dishes. I could eat only a little; I sat and stared out into the garden. The coolness of the night was still on the tall hibiscus against the garden fence. The air plants dripped with the early morning drenching which Tomas had given them; the palms rustled with a sound like rain; Culion Bay lay gray in the shadows of the dawn. The crest of Coron was slowly taking on the color of gold as the sun climbed higher. Soon it would be full day; soon the tropic coolness would roll westward, and the tropic heat would roll in like the sea, covering everything. My last day in Culion had begun.

I had left certain things until the last minute. I would see Manson and the Padre. Both had been my unfailing friends. They had done much, these two, towards my well-being. Manson, I thought, counted me among his converts. And at that, he might be right. Something had stood by me throughout the years, something was standing by me now, as I started through the gate. I had given my car to José; on this journey I would walk.

The dogs were at my heels. I hadn't the heart to turn them back. It would be a long trek for Mame, but she begged to come. Both knew full well that I did not allow them to follow me through the colony. . . . They knew somehow that this was different. We three started along the road that led to Rizal Plaza. At every break in the tropic foliage I stopped and looked at the harbor. Beauty! I had looked upon this beauty day and night, day and night. The road rounded the point and dropped down past the Protestant Chapel. Slowly I climbed its steps. Leon, who was Manson's assistant, was just coming through the doorway.

"Good morning, Mr. Ferguson. We are going to miss you very much."

"Thank you, Leon. Is the Reverend in?"

"He is within the church. Please to go in."

How cool and pleasant it was in the high-ceiled building! In the dim light, pews and altar were faintly outlined. Manson came down the aisle.

"I'm glad you have come, Ned. I came here very early this morning to pray that you would have a safe and pleasant journey."

My tongue seemed thick. I put my hand on Shag's head and tried to speak. He went right on. "This is something I got for you the last time I was in Manila. It is my best gift, a Bible."

He placed in my clumsy hands a tissue covered box. I stammered thanks. He saw how shaky I was, and asked, although he knew, what time the boat was coming. We could not say good-by, the word would not come. Manson laid his hand on my shoulder for an instant. That was all.

It was quite a walk to the Catholic church. All along the road were people, my friends. They nodded, murmured a "Good morning," and smiled. They hid their emotion with silence. I was glad that they did not stop to talk. I could not stand much of this. My own voice seemed to have gone. In response I could only nod, and wave a friendly hand. At last I reached the church and began to climb the long, wide steps. From above came a cheery call. I looked up. The Padre was coming down to meet me, his robes flapping about his feet.

"Ned, you rascal! You wouldn't go without a special visit, would you? Is it a bit of wine you come for, or is it to see the old man?" He gave me a friendly punch. "What do you think, you heathen? I said early Mass for you this morning!"

I swallowed a lump in my throat. He talked on about my work, giving me much more credit than I deserved. In all these years it had made no difference to him that I was of another faith. Another? In that moment I knew that all faiths were one.

I tried to say so, but my voice quavered, and he, much more master of himself than I, smiled. "Go on with you. And behave yourself, or we'll bring you back to Culion in chains." He was off, down the street, on his way.

This business of leaving a place that had been home for half a lifetime was not so simple. I was heading for Dr. Taborada's office. Something of what the Padre said was true. I had worked here to some purpose. The current that lit the streets through which I passed; the food that might be eaten without fear because of the ice that preserved it; the comforts that were possible because of the throbbing plant down by the sea; in these things I had played a vital part. Well, the plant would go on without me; I had trained José thoroughly.

I took the lower road along the sea. We three, the dogs and I, were very tired.

Under the great trees at the gate it was cooler. This was the hour for food tickets and the people were waiting for their share. The few I passed along the road had been shy. But here numbers gave them courage. Some called to me as I went through the gate.

"Take me to America with you, Mr. Ferguson?"

"Better stay in Culion."

"Hope you return to us, sometime."

As I came to the house of the Chief Clerk, Mrs. Villa called from her veranda.

"A safe journey. I wish we too were bound for America."

The boys standing about the post office cried cheerily, "Good luck, Mr. Ferguson."

The dogs and I turned into the lane that led through rows of low flowers to the Administration Building. Dr. Taborada was in his office. I saw him in his immaculate white, bending over his desk near the window. Before I called he looked up. At once he came to the window.

"How goes it, Ned?"

There were a few last arrangements to be made for the plant. We went over them.

"José is fully able to take charge," I assured him.

The word of my coming had gone around and others of the administration staff came to the windows to greet me. Dr. Taborada made a little speech praising my work. They applauded and called farewells.

As I turned away, I found myself comparing my leave-taking here with that of a well man who had lived and worked in any place for most of his life. There seemed just one difference. We talked through windows.

The way to the power plant was long but the road was level by the sea. When we came to the rise we went slowly.

Mame was weary. My spirit mounted as I came to the place that seemed my very own. The machinery was humming away, and each boy was at his job. José with his accustomed smile, which showed a wide expanse of very white teeth, was self-conscious. As the new manager, he received the old one with embarrassment. I strolled about; the boys began to whisper and giggle.

"Chief, will you come into your office?" José begged. I went slowly to the room that seemed still mine. My desk had been cleared, and square in its center was a carved wooden replica of our old plant, our first plant, which had wrought a revolution in Culion. It was a faithful copy, with one addition. On a sign hanging on the miniature gate, there was added a line.

COLONY ELECTRIC POWER AND FISHING COMPANY
NED FERGUSON. NO. 1 BOSS.

This was for me, to be carried to the States. It was a wonderful piece of work. I faced my boys and looked over that group of begrimed leper engineers and workmen who had labored with me year in and year out. They were waiting. I opened my mouth to speak. Nothing came. Then I pounded hard upon the desk and yelled.

"Get the hell out of here and go to work!"

With a burst of laughter they scrambled out, and I was left with José.

"It will be on the boat, Chief," he assured me, "when you go."

The whistle of the *Don Juan* was sounding, faint and far away, when I got back home. There was scarcely more than an hour left. I called the dogs to my bedroom and closed the door. Then I went out, alone, to prepare the trench. Tomas was invisible. The *Don Juan* was just passing the reefs. It was now. I brought Mame out and as I patted her, thrust in the tiny needle Dr. Ravino said would hardly be felt. He had assured me that it would be swift, and merciful. But how swift!

I laid her body within the trench and covered her. I was faint, but I could give myself no time. I went for Shag. As I stooped over him, he raised his eyes, closed them, and lay down with a long sigh. May my release be like that.

I sat there for a few minutes looking at the mound under the flaming hibiscus. There was still no sign of Tomas but I knew that he had watched. The little steamer shrilled a prolonged blast. That meant it was nearing the pier. I stood up and looked long at my garden. I pulled myself together, said good-by to Shag and Mame. On the porch I found Tomas, waiting.

"Your bags are ready, sir. Shall I take them to the boat?"

"No, Tomas, I have made other plans. I want always to think of you here. This home is yours. You are to live here until the day you leave Culion to join Carmen."

Tomas, usually so fluent, found it difficult to speak.

"You are good to me. Sir, it will always be your house."

"When you leave, I have made certain arrangements for you. The Chief knows."

A boy came to the steps. He held out a note. It was from Dr. Taborada.

"Our plans have been changed. Instead of boarding the boat at the Balala pier we have decided to carry you out by the small boat from the colony wharf. Do not trouble about your baggage—just come to the landing in a half hour."

Mischief was afoot but I had no choice. A half hour! I wandered through my house, the porch, the hall, the kitchen. It was my home, the home I had achieved against sickness, against loneliness, against despair, against everything a man could have to fight. I was proud of that home.

There was a short blast from the *Don Juan's* whistle. My half hour was up. Tomas was at the gate. The raucous blare of a horn broke the stillness. I took one look and burst into laughter. It was José in my old car, now his. But for José I might not have known the car. It was swathed from radiator-cap to taillight with red, white and blue bunting tied on with ribbons of all colors. Two huge flags, the Philippine flag and my Stars and Stripes, were crossed in front of the radiator and waved above it. Directly over the radiator was a card on which someone had painted a bon voyage. On the bunting at the left and right of the car were signs wishing me a safe journey, in Visayan and Tagalog, and on the back in Ilocano, the three languages of the Philippines, all represented in the seven thousand patients of the colony. My throat ached. José in his excitement applied the brakes too sharply and the car skidded in the sand.

"I am to take you to the pier," he called. He jumped out, bowed, and opened the rear door for me. As I went through the gate I half turned.

"Tomas, my son, good-by. I have never prayed much, but I shall pray every day that soon your faith and Carmen's will be rewarded and that you two will be together."

I barely caught his whisper.

"Good-by, sir."

I was laughing so as not to cry. I slammed the rear door shut, pushed José into the front seat, and climbed in beside him, waving to Tomas, as we started off with the horn going full blast, around and down the hill, by Rizal Plaza and down to the inner bay.

The streets were empty, a strange thing for this time of day. As we took the turn to the beach, I saw why. They were all there. Along the roadway were lines of Boy Scouts and Camp Fire Girls who saluted gravely as we passed. On the pier stood the band. As José stopped the car they burst forth with "Hail to the Chief." The crowd waved and shouted. The harbor was thick with small craft. There were more than a hundred boats and balsa rafts, each contributing its bit of color with flags and bunting. Sebastian Llanos, who was now President of the Council, was the orator. He spoke briefly of the comfort brought by the plant, and of our comradeship. He waved his arms to the colonists, the massed craft in the harbor, the band, the Boy Scouts and the Camp Fire Girls. With a sweeping gesture that included the whole assembly, he concluded, "All of us will miss you."

I replied. It was not much of a speech. But what I tried to say of the ache in my heart at leaving lifetime friends, they understood. They were silent for a moment when I finished. Then the Presidente, the Chief of Police and José escorted me to the colony boat while all the members of the police force busied themselves shooing away the small craft so as to provide a lane for our passage. The motor roared; our boatmen cast off, and we backed slowly from the small pier. The band was playing "The Stars and Stripes Forever." I stood up, maintaining a precarious balance as I waved. Cheers resounded from the shore and from the boats that paddled furiously to keep up with us. And so, surrounded by this triumphal armada, I saw my last of the colony of the lepers at Culion.

Ten minutes, and I had boarded the *Don Juan*. A place had been assigned to me on the after-deck. My luggage was all there. I stood by the rail and looked down on the Balala pier. To my amazement, almost every doctor and nurse in the place, Manson, the Padre, Sister Victoire and her associates, it seemed as if all of that large group of well people who ministered to us on the Island had come to see me off. Dr. Taborada and Dr. Ravino saw me at the rail and began waving. Then they all joined in. My heart was pounding. Hardly knowing what I did I raised my right arm stiffly in the old salute of the soldier. And at that moment, the hawsers splashed into the water, the boat began moving away. The whistle at the plant was shrilling, the land was slipping by. The group on the pier grew smaller and smaller.

Twenty-five years of a man's life on that little island. What did it mean, I asked myself stupidly as I stood there clutching the rail? But within me welled the answer born of those years. Life, no matter how it is lived, is always a mystery. To take it as it comes, asking no quarter, fighting to the end, that is the creed the quarter century had brought to me. Balancing the scales at the end of twenty-five years in a leper colony, this leper knows that he is, first of all, a man. For that man life has been worth while. Adios, Culion!

CHAPTER ✦ ✦ ✦ ✦ ✦ ✦ ✦ THIRTY-THREE

CARITA, MY DARLING:

Wednesday I reach Carville. I have an attendant from the health service who will mail this.

I'm afraid that my letter to you just before I left Culion was not very cheerful. It was not easy to say good-by to the long life I had there. I can write you more cheerfully now since oddly enough I am living in a strange kind of triumph. There's one phrase that keeps going through my mind—it began with the clanking of the engines of the *Don Juan* on the way to Manila. When we reached the army transport its powerful motors took up the same refrain. All through the long journey across the seas from Manila to San Francisco, as I lay secluded in my cabin, I heard it. Now under my compartment in this fast express, the wheels are singing—"I'm going home—going home."

The journey has given me time to think, alone, for who would come near me? Alone I have looked back over those

years of life in death. . . . What did they bring? First, torture—a kind of madness. Then a return to sanity, not the
sanity I had known, but one related to my new world
within a world. Kindness, Carita, that memory overlays all
the rest. Kindness to those of us stricken, from those who
chose to minister to us. Untiring doctors and nurses, im-
bued with the spirit of healing, contacting us who were a
menace, risking infection, trying only to help. Out of this
kindness, wonder! For you and I have been permitted to see
the beginning of a miracle. It was coming, the relief sought
for thousands of years. At first so painful that it could
hardly be endured. Then mitigated, little by little, but still
calling for endurance against—a chance. Not a sure cure but
the chance of arresting the progress of the living death. We
watched hundreds of men, women and children leave us
and our little city of the doomed, to return to the normal
world. And then you went. You, better than most, know
because of your work with the paroles, how some of them,
forgetting in the joy of their return, the care essential to its
preservation, would be sent back to us, perhaps to go forth
again, perhaps to stay. Yet they had left and none had
left before.

As we watched them go, how many times you and I
talked of the future when such death in life shall be no
more. How, working patiently, as they have always worked,
the doctors would find a surer cure, ten, fifty, a hundred
years hence.

I am content, Carita. As I look from my window at the
land I love and which I had never expected to see again,
joy pervades me.

This train speeds through fields, far-reaching plains, the

little towns that mean home, my home. I have seen them
often in dreams, particularly since you went away. As a
ghostly wraith I have traveled again and again through the
land I love so well. In prison one dreams much of home.
Today I am liberated.

The door of my compartment is opened only when the
attendant brings in my food. If those outside knew who
rides here, terror and panic would seize them. But they do
not know. Those in charge have seen to it that every pre-
caution has been taken.

In the flesh I am still in prison. But the essential "I" has
escaped. I am free. My spirit is out in the fields, in the
woods, running through the towns. I am living my youth,
the youth that followed the flag to the Orient nearly forty
years ago. All the years of suffering, of horror, of hope and
despair, fade into oblivion. Tomorrow this train, and I in
it, will pass through the very town where I was born!

I may get a glimpse of the little stream where Tom and
I fished for sun perch, of the tiny strip of woods where a
gang of us with a scrawny hound chased rabbits, and with
good luck treed a possum or a coon. I shall pass the open
fields at the edge of the town, and the water tower. Main
Street running past the station. Old darky Watts with his
fleabitten nag and his tumbling-to-pieces hack. The Ma-
jestic Hotel over the poolroom, two-storied brick—perhaps
none of them will be there—but I shall see them! If I look
quickly enough I may catch a glimpse of our house on a
little hill in a grove of maples, a half mile east of the tracks.
The rambling old house that has been home to us for three
generations.

I press my face against the screened window. Across the

gray expanses seen through the mists of evening, I see my dreams take form. There are faces, the faces of those who by my own intent and scheming believed me with the actual dead these many years. My mother. I left her one morning without good-by. She thought I had gone for a day. I can see her lined face growing older; her eyes look into mine. I believe she knows now. But I had to come this close to see.

How strange it is that those who, as you know, are still among the living, Mabel and Jane, are the two who are most unreal. Mother, father and Tom—they seem to be with me. They would have loved you, Carita.

Dear, dear Little Face, I once thought I would bring you with me when I came, but I had to leave you on the other side of the world.

I'm tired. I must sleep. Good night, my love.

NED.

PARAGRAPHS FROM A SOUTHERN
NEWSPAPER

New Orleans, Louisiana: The body of Ned Langford, a veteran of the Spanish-American War, who contracted leprosy while serving in the Philippines, was taken from a compartment on the express when it arrived in this city . last night. Langford was being transferred from Culion, the leper island of the Philippines, to the Federal Leprosarium at Carville. The ex-soldier had been isolated during the entire journey, for the protection of passengers. The Federal Health Officer who accompanied him stated that his patient had died shortly after the train entered Louisiana. Langford seemed reasonably well the previous day except that he was greatly excited because the train had passed through his home town and he had seen the house in which he was born. He evidently died because of an overburdened heart, heavily taxed by years of strain.

Langford will be buried with military honors. The body will be interred in the U. S. National Cemetery at Baton Rouge. A number of former service men who became lepers are buried there.

NED LANGFORD'S STORY IS ONLY A PARTIAL PICTURE OF THE TRAGEDY OF HANSEN'S DISEASE (LEPROSY). THE FOLLOWING PAGES CARRY A PERSONAL MESSAGE FROM THE AUTHOR—WITHOUT WHICH THE READER CANNOT KNOW THE ENTIRE STORY.

A PERSONAL MESSAGE FROM
THE AUTHOR

SINCE my purpose in telling the story of Ned Langford is to correct erroneous ideas about Hansen's disease (leprosy), I owe it to the reader to explain that to know of the people and life on Culion is not to know the entire story of this disease.

It is estimated that there are three to five million of its victims in the world today: of this vast number less than three per cent are cared for in any colony or hospital. Of every hundred ill, ninety-seven wander in the fields or the market places seeking a beggar's subsistence, being driven out of every place where they are found; feared and shunned by mankind generally.

Even those who enjoy a refuge of any kind are seldom as well cared for as are the patients at Culion or at the United States leprosarium at Carville, Louisiana.

I have seen them herded together in hovels on the edge of an unsanitary swamp, on spray-drenched islands in the sea, or on muddy banks of a river. I have seen them in Bali, isolated, alone, in decaying grass lean-tos in the jungle. In Indo-China I have visited "dumps"—it would be misleading to name them anything else—where a thousand miserable, heavy cases, without the ministration of a single well person, cook, nurse, or doctor, just sat about, contemplating the disintegration of their own bodies and those of their fellows.

In Korea I saw a hopelessly crippled woman walk out of a leprosarium to a life of beggary to make room for her son for whom, without her sacrifice, there was no place and no possibility of treatment.

These unfortunates should, at least, have freedom from fear, but even in our own enlightened country—even after they are dismissed as negative cases—fear follows them. The doors of the leprosarium open but the doors of the world remain closed in their faces. Ignorance, misunderstanding, age-old myths and

302

superstitions, operate to make life intolerable. It is not too much to say that the effects of this attitude are far more disastrous to these individuals and their families than the disease itself. We are still a people hypnotized by a word—the word leper. Until we understand clearly the true meaning of that word, until we grasp the facts of the disease, we will continue to be guilty of cruelty and injustice—only the truth can set them free.

It was the pressing need to uncover those facts, to find that truth, that brought into existence the Leonard Wood Memorial.

In 1927, following the death of Leonard Wood, then Governor-General of the Philippines, "The Leonard Wood Memorial" was created. It is the only organization devoting its entire efforts, on an international basis, to scientific studies dealing with the problem of Hansen's disease (leprosy). Its purpose is to seek, through scientific investigations, the means to eradicate this disease. Its motto is—"To leave no scientific step untaken that holds any promise of finding the solution to this age-old curse of the human race." Medical science is the only hope for these stricken ones.

Trustees and members of the Advisory Medical Board are individuals occupying the highest positions of public trust in business and in medical and scientific fields. These give generously of their time to this work without compensation.

The history of the Memorial is one of work and of achievement. Through the publication of the *International Journal of Leprosy*, the latest information on the progress of science in combating the disease is sent to workers all over the world. This is the only means by which the isolated doctor in a remote leprosy colony can keep abreast of new methods of treatment.

A pathological laboratory is maintained at Culion, Philippines, to study the essential nature of the disease, especially the structural and functional changes which it causes.

A bacteriological and biochemical laboratory is supported and staffed by the Memorial at Harvard Medical School.

Epidemiological studies are carried on in endemic areas to investigate the environmental conditions under which the disease occurs and is transmitted.

Clinical trials and controlled studies of new drugs are being encouraged in co-operation with leading leprologists.

A department of information and photography is maintained to aid in the dissemination of information for the lay public in an attempt to correct the widespread, erroneous ideas about Hansen's disease (leprosy). It is far less dangerous to public health than many other diseases, and those suffering from it should be treated as sick people, not as criminals.

We believe that if everyone could know the story of Ned Langford, the attitude toward these pitiful, ill people would change and an interest would be created which would eventually drive this ancient scourge from the earth.

We therefore hope that we can find it possible to send WHO WALK ALONE to many more thousands, though the cost to the Memorial is considerable despite the fact that the publishers have waived their profits and the author his royalties.

The Leonard Wood Memorial depends entirely on contributions from the general public for its financial support.

"Erie Vista"
Geneva on the Lake
Ohio

SOME OF THE QUESTIONS COMMONLY ASKED ABOUT HANSEN'S DISEASE

Q. What is Hansen's disease?

A. Hansen's disease is a systemic infection (affecting the whole body), but has a particular affinity for the skin and nerves.

Q. Are there any other names for Hansen's disease?

A. Yes. Leprosy is the age-old term, but because of the widespread and exaggerated fear associated with this word, the term "Hansen's disease" is now preferred for popular usage. The disease is called "La Lepre" in French, "Aussatz" in German, and "Spedalskhed" in Norwegian.

Q. Is the causative agent known?

A. It is generally accepted that the disease is caused by the *mycobacterium leprae*, discovered by Gerhard Armauer Hansen in 1871.

Q. Can the bacilli be grown outside the human body?

A. Since Hansen's isolation of the bacillus, hundreds of attempts have been made to culture the organism but to date none of these has successfully met the requirements for proof.

Q. Where is the disease found?

A. It is found mostly in tropical and subtropical regions, with residual areas of low prevalence in cooler regions. The most heavily infected localities are in tropical Africa, India, China, South-east Asia, Japan, Oceania (excepting Australia, New Zealand, and Tasmania), the Dutch East Indies, the Philippines, and in certain parts of Central and South America. Cases to a limited degree are found in almost all countries.

Q. How many cases of Hansen's disease are there in the world today?

A. While no properly supervised surveys have been possible, except in isolated instances, the generally accepted number is from three to five million.

Q. Does Hansen's disease exist in the United States?

A. Some cases arise in Florida, Louisiana, Texas, and southern California. Occasional cases discovered in the North are usually imports. The estimated total is from one to two thousand.

Q. Does the United States provide leprosaria?

A. Yes. Six are maintained by the United States, its Territories, and Dependencies. An excellent leprosarium, under the direction of the Public Health Service, is maintained by the United States at Carville, Louisiana. It is staffed by personnel of the Service and by Sisters of Charity. It has a modern laboratory for routine work and scientific investigation. There are also leprosaria in the Hawaiian Islands, Puerto Rico, St. Croix in the Virgin Islands, the Canal Zone, and for the Trust Territory of the Pacific, in Tinian, Marianas.

Q. How many patients are there at Carville?

A. There are approximately four hundred. The number varies slightly from time to time.

Q. At what age does the disease usually occur?

A. Hansen's disease is usually contracted in childhood, but adults occasionally contract it.

Q. Are males more susceptible than females?

A. A higher attack rate among males is the rule for the lepromatous form of the disease.

Q. What are the sources of infection of Hansen's disease?

A. The only known sources of infection are human beings suffering from the lepromatous ("open") form of the disease.

Q. How is Hansen's disease spread?

A. This is not known. The bacilli are present in nasal discharges and scrapings from the skin of patients. Possibly they are inhaled or swallowed or they may enter healthy persons through wounds in the skin.

Q. Is the disease easily transmitted?

A. Although the disease is infectious, intimate contact of a susceptible person with an ill individual apparently is required. Physicians, nurses, and attendants in leprosaria rarely contract Hansen's disease. Infection of husband or wife from an infected spouse is likewise rare.

Q. Is the disease hereditary?

A. No.

Q. Is the disease congenital?

A. No.

Q. Is it true that the incubation period for Hansen's disease often covers many years?

A. Hansen's disease is noted for its long incubation period, which may be a matter of months or even several years. It is thought that the average incubation period is four or five years, although intervals of thirty years have been reported.

Q. Are there different types of Hansen's disease?

A. According to accepted international classification there are two main types of the disease, "lepromatous" and "tuberculoid." A subclassification is also recognized and is known as "incharacteristic" or "indeterminate." From the Public Health standpoint, the classification is closed for the tuberculoid type and open for the lepromatous type. The *closed* cases are considered non-infectious.

Q. Is the disease fatal?

A. Not as a rule. The patient usually succumbs to some other cause. There are known cases where individuals are still living after forty years of illness.

Q. Is the disease painful?

A. Usually the patient suffers little from the disease itself. Nerve involvement, however, may be extremely painful and there is much discomfort caused by various complications.

Q. Can Hansen's disease be cured?

A. No drug has been proved to cure the disease. Consequently, the word "arrested" is used in preference to "cured." In recent years it has been found that drugs of the sulfone group, promin, diasone, and sulphetrone, are the best therapeutic agents, but it is not yet known whether the clinical improvement which follows their use will be permanent.

Q. Why are people so afraid of Hansen's disease?

A. That is a question to which no satisfactory answer can be given, since there is nothing in the disease to justify its being accorded such a special place of horror in the minds of the people. Its point of infection is so low that a premeditated attempt on the part of the average individual to inoculate himself or to infect himself with the disease by association with sick persons would, in all probability, not meet with success. An advanced case of the disease is not pleasant to look upon, but the same may be said for many other diseases which do not share in this almost universal repugnance. A very large proportion of patients bear little or no outer signs of their affliction.

Q. Can anything be done to combat this attitude?

A. (a) One of the most effective means is a more extended use of the name "Hansen's disease" instead of "leprosy." The International Leprosy Congress held at Havana in 1948 recommended that the name "leper" should be abandoned.

(b) Dissemination of information about the nature of the disease.

Q. What is the most encouraging factor in the campaign?

A. The attention which is now being given to scientific studies of the nature and control of Hansen's disease is the most encouraging factor. The discovery of a specific "preventive" or "cure" would solve the whole problem.

INDEX

Africa, leprosy in, 225
Agramonte, Dr. Aristides, 51-2
Aguilar, Tomas. (See Tomas)
Aguinaldo, Emilio, 12, 13-14
Angkor-Tom, 224
Angkor-Wat, 224
Aniline dyes, as cure for leprosy, 225
Anti-leprosy campaign, 308
Apo, Leonard Wood's yacht, 201
Arang, Frederico, 157, 179, 193, 225
Armistice, World War, 195-98

"Baguio," 271-75
Balala, 99, 239, 247; and Lepers' Riot, 248-50
Balala pier, 194, 241, 291, 294
Banaue, 13
Benguet, 144, 244
Bond, Dr. Jack: and Cebu Leprosarium, 239-42; helps Ned go home, 283-84; meets Ned, 218-20; returns to Culion, 221-26; warns Ned about health, 278
Bond, Mrs. Jack, mission to United States, 238
Bonifacio, Andres, 265
Bonifacio, Francisco, 265-69
Bontoc, 13
Boy Scouts, 293
Brant, Peter, 207-13, 242, 280
Brillas, Santiago, 178-79
Busuanga, 96, 122

Cabisan, Victor, 178-79, 272, 278
Calavite Straits, 93
Caloocan, 12, 47
Camp Fire Girls, 293
Cañete, Pedro, 182
Carita, 15, 18, 20-1, 118, 124, 180, 185, 265, 270-76; and marriage, 173-74; and Ned, 163-76; pronounced negative, 190-94; returns to Culion, 255-59; work with negatives, 255-57
Carmen, 187-90, 220, 243, 251-52; leaves Culion second time, 276;

marriage of, 257-69; and the typhoon, 270-75
Carroll, James, 52
Caruso, Enrico, 67
Carville, Federal Leprosarium, 53, 283, 299; number of patients at, 305
Cavite, 8
Cebu, 118, 151, 187, 189, 239-40, 246
Chaulmoogra, 64, 140, 162, 219, 223-25, 234, 242
China, leprosy in, 304
China, U.S.S., 6, 76, 232
China Sea, 96, 128
Chinese lepers, 106
Cholera, 93, 162, 268
Clemente, Fra Juan, 83-4
Colon, U.S.S., 7
Colony Hall, 121
Cordova, 188
Coron, 96, 122, 128-32, 169, 286
Corregidor, 8, 79
Crisolaya, Bernabe, 192
Crisolgo, Dr., 141, 160
Cruz, José, 156, 178, 209, 244, 247, 262, 264, 271-73, 278, 290, 292-93
Culion, 91, 96-7, 128; building in colony, 221, 238-39; description of, 96-7, 105-6; justice in, 228-31; leper colony, 28, 53, 92; medical directors at, 116, 162; movies in, 270; quarantine of new patients in, 102
Culion Bay, 286
Culion Harbor, 96-7, 122
Cuyo, 271

Da Vinci, Leonardo, 261
Dean, William H., 51-2
Dengue fever, 158-59, 166
Devil's Island, 193
Dickson, Dr., 29-30, 33, 36
Dominguez, Dr., 221, 233, 241-42, 246, 255

Don Juan, S.S., 290-92, 294, 295
Drake, Sir Francis, 83
Dresden Museum, 262

Encephalitis, 277
Epidemiology, 237

Ferguson, Ned. (See Ned)
Filipinos: characteristics of, 10, 82, 89, 105, 122-23, 141, 234; dress of, 120-21, 264; languages of, 292
Finlay, Dr. Carlos Juan, 51   [210
Fishing business at Culion, 177-80,
Fish traps, 178
Forbes, Cameron, 199
Fourth of July, observance of, in Culion, 152
Franklin, Benjamin, 261
Funston, Frederick, 14

Geronimo, 5
Gold, called in by United States, 278-81
Gravina, S.S., 271, 275
Greene, Francis Vinton, 6

Hansen, Gerhard Armauer, 49, 303
Hansen bacillus, 40
"Hansen's disease," 303-8
Hudson, Reverend, 151-53, 217
Hydnocarpus, 224

Iceland, leprosy in, 225
Iloilo, 144, 187
Independence, Filipino attitude toward, 152-53
India, leprosy in, 225, 304
Insurrectos, 11, 13
Intong, Bruno, 180
Intramuros, 9

Jacildo, Ricardo, 178-79, 219-20, 272
Jane, 22-5, 27-8, 44, 50, 57-8, 72, 77-8, 255
Java, leprosy in, 100
Jolo, 207

Katipuman, the, 266
Kent, Dr., 85
Khmer kings, 224

Lambert, Richard, 207-13
Langford, Ned. (See Ned)
Langford, Tom, 17-18, 20-1, 23-5, 31-3, 56-61, 155, 161, 184-85
La Rosa, Hilario, 151
Lazear, Dr. Jesse W., 51-2
Lechon, 230-31, 263-64
Leper "parole," 180-81, 190-94
Leper reaction, 77-8
Lepers: appearance of, 70-1; babies of, 170-71; marriage among, 257-65; as negatives, 180-81, 190-94, 255-57; number of, 225, 304; quarantine of, 102; United States care for, 304-5; work for, 107, 225
Lepers, work of, 106-7; on colony buildings, 221, 239; fishing company, 177-80; Ned's plan for, 147-50; as nurses, 239; power plant, 194-95; refrigerating plant, 186, 261; working project begins, 156-58
Lepers' Home, 12, 37, 52
Lepers' Riot, 245-53
Leprosaria: at Carville, Louisiana, 53, 200, 304-5 (see also Carville, Federal Leprosarium); at Cebu (see Cebu); at Culion (see Culion); in Hawaiian Islands, 304; in Puerto Rico, 304; in Virgin Islands, 304
Leprosy, 21, 31-3, 37-8, 40-1, 48-50; cause of, 236-37, 305; chances of infection, 114, 204, 235-37, 306; cure of, 225-26, 307; diagnosis of, 40, 85; extent of, 50, 93, 100, 225, 236, 304; fatal, 102, 307; fear of, 21, 33-49, 202, 204, 235, 240, 256, 306-7; foci of, 100; heavy cases, 123-25; hereditary, 306; ignorance of, 49-50; incubation period of, 306; larger incidence in tropics, 236; myths about, 235; the name, 256-57, 303; painful, 307; research in, 209, 223-26, 237, 308; sex susceptibility to, 305; spreading of, 235-37; transmission of, 204, 235-37, 306; treatments, 140-42, 162, 242-43 (see also Chaulmoogra);

types of, 306; in United States, 50, 100, 304-5; work against, 225-26, 239, 308

Leprosy, remedies for: aniline dyes, 225; chaulmoogra (see Chaulmoogra); methylene blue, 225

Liberty Bonds, United States, 184

Llanos, Sebastian, 293

Louisiana State Home for Lepers, 50 (see also Carville, Federal Leprosarium)

Lubang, 93

Mactan, 188, 251

Magellan, Ferdinand, 188

Malacañan Palace, 9, 221

Malaria, 162, 268

Manila, 9-10, 81-2

Manila Bay, 8, 10, 78-9

Manson, Pastor, 217, 263, 266, 286-87, 294

Marello, Father, 103, 116-19, 161, 163-65, 175, 183, 191-93, 195, 217, 263, 288, 294

Marshall, Dr. James, 92-6, 99-102, 113-14, 154, 161-62

Mateo, 210-14

Mathewson, Christy, 67

McGraw's pennant winners, 67

Methylene blue, 225

Metropolitan Opera House, 67

Miguel, Conrado, 227-31

Mindanao, 28, 207, 262, 276

Mindoro, 93, 94, 207-8, 210-14

Morales, Dr., 228-31

Moros, 28, 233

Mount Polis, 13

Mycobacterium leprae, 303

Napoleonic law, 229-30

Ned: appearance of spots, 24, 28-33; and Bob Sellars, 3, 5, 7-9, 143-45; in business, 20-1, 23-4, 26, 31; and Carita, 163-67, 169-70, 173-76, 190-94, 255-57, 276, 295-298 (see also Carita); death of, 299; discovers he has leprosy, 40-1; finds blue orchid, 128-32; gets dengue fever, 158-59; gets engaged, 22; goes to Culion, 74-80, 91-8; his house in Culion,

107-8, 116, 132-38; hunts tamarau, 207-15; leaves Culion, 286-94; makes own armistice, 196-98; meets Leonard Wood, 201-5; in New York, 63-73; at San Lazaro, 84-91; sees Sancho, 123-25; and Spanish-American War, 3-18; takes treatments, 140-42, 242-43; and Tomas, 86-7, 113, 259-60, 264-65 (see also Tomas); and the typhoon, 271-75; wants to go home, 283-84; warns Balala of revolt, 247-48; and work for lepers, 147-50, 155-58, 177-80, 186, 194-95, 202-4, 219, 221, 261, 289-90 (see also Lepers, work of); and World War, 182-85

"Negative House," 181

Nipa houses, 10

Nolasco, Carita. (See Carita)

Nolasco, Maximino, 18, 28, 39

Nolasco, Sancho. (See Sancho)

Noli Me Tangere, by José Rizal, 261

Norway, leprosy in, 225

Order of St. Francis, 83

Padre Marello. (See Marello, Father)

Palao, Dr., 215

Pasig River, 9, 10, 82, 83

Philippine Health Service, 53, 92

Philippine Insurrection, 11-14, 39, 47

Philippine Islands: death rate in, 268; description of, 13-14, 94; independence of, 152-53, 266-69; progress in, 267-68

Philippines, University of the, 218

Plaza Libertad, 121, 155, 182, 195. (See also Rizal Plaza)

Ponce, Dr., 218, 221, 243, 258

Power plant at Culion, 194-95

Public Health Service, United States, 283

Puerta Princessa, 271

Puerto Rico, leprosy in, 100

Ramos, Pedro, 215

Ravino, Dr., 77, 79-86, 281, 285, 294

Reed, Dr. Walter, 51-2

Refrigerating plant at Culion, 186, 194, 261
Revolt, effect of, in Balala, 248-50
Rice terraces in the Philippines, 14
Rigadon, 264
Rizal, José, 261-62, 267-69   [261
Rizal Day, 152, 160, 166, 168, 259,
Rizal Plaza, 287, 293. (See also Plaza Libertad)
Robinson, Captain, 77
Roosevelt, Theodore, 5
Rough Riders, Roosevelt's, 5

St. Francis, Order of, 83
St. Paul de Chartres, Sisters of, 102
Sancho, 21, 28, 103, 117-18, 123-24, 126
San Jacinto, battle of, 13
San Lazaro, 48, 81-6, 157, 235, 277
Santez, Marciano, 227-31
San Tomas, University of, 157
Sellars, Bob, 3, 5, 20, 27-8, 143-45, 243-44
Senator, U.S.S., 6
Sidney, Dr., 75, 76-80
Simpson, Walter, 181-82, 186, 194-95, 209, 233, 277
Sisters of St. Paul de Chartres, 102
Smallpox, 93, 162, 268
Socorro, 241
Surabaya, Java, 260
Syphilis, 235

Taborada, Dr. Demetrio, 246, 247, 251, 260, 263, 266, 268, 289, 291, 294
Taft, William Howard, 269
Tagalogs, 210
Tamarau, 94, 207-8, 210-15
"Terrace of the Leper King, The," 224
Thompson, Major Bill, 38-42, 45-61, 82, 184-85, 196, 200
Todd, Dr., 61, 63-5, 68
Tolino, Carmen. (See Carmen)
Tolino, Vicente. (See Vicente)
Tomas, 86-7, 89, 92-8; assistant to Ned in business, 278; becomes Ned's house boy, 109-113; and fighting cock, 151-52, 155-56,

159-60; gets stock in the company, 262; marriage of, 257-69; mother's visit, 168-69; saves Carmen's life, 187; says good-by to Ned, 292-93; studies accounting, 244; and United States gold, 280
Treasury Department, United States, 281
Typhoon, 271-75

Umali, Francisco, 179
United States: entry into World War, 182-85; leprosy in, 50, 100, 303; Liberty Bonds, 184; World War Armistice, 195-98
United States Public Health Service, 283
United States Treasury Department, 281
United States War Department, 283
University of the Philippines, 218
University of San Tomas, 157
Utah Light Artillery, 47

Vicente, 188-89, 220-21, 227, 245-46, 251-53, 273, 275
Victoire, Sister, 125, 191-92, 232-33, 235, 294
Villariosa, Nurse, 188
Visitors' Day, 254

War Department, United States, 283
Watkins, Dr., 36-9
Wilkinson, 104-5, 116
Windle, Horace, 20, 24-5, 29, 31
Winton, Dr., 102, 104-9, 114-16, 135, 137, 146-50, 153-55, 180, 190, 200-1, 283-84
Wood, Leonard, 5, 199, 201-5, 217, 232-33, 238; monument at Culion, 265
World War, United States, entry into, 182-85; Armistice, 195-98

Yaws, 235
Yellow fever, 51

Zanilla, Manuel, 87, 156
Zealandia, U.S.S., 7

*Leonard Wood Memorial
One Madison Avenue
New York 10, N. Y.*

1. First Colony Gate (lower level)
2. School House
3. Power Plant
4. Chemical Plant
5. Clinic No. I
6. Emergency Hospital No. I
7. Women's Dormitory
8. Catholic Church
9. Harbor Light
10. Girls' Dormitories under care of Chaplain
11. General Hospital Ward No. 3
12. General Hospital Wards Nos. I & 2 (upper story built by the Memorial)
13. General Hospital Ward No. 4
14. Long Cement Stairs
15. X-Ray Clinic
16. Former Laboratory (now McKinley Memorial Library and office of the Chief Clinician)
17. Wood Memorial Laboratory
18. Quarantine Building
19. Small Wharf
20. Emergency Hospital No. 3
21. Protestant Chapel
22. Colony Hall
23. Kitchen
24. Tenement Houses around Plaza Libertad (Rizal Plaza)
25. Rizal's Monument
26. Broad Cement Stairs
27. Wood's Monument
28. Clinic No. 2
29. Theater
30. Protestant Dormitories and Hospital
31. Emergency Hospital No. 3
32. Second Colony Gate (upper story)
33. Catholic Chaplain's Residence and Chapel
34. Children's Home
35. Sisters' Residence
36. Residence of the Chief of the Colony
37. Residence of one of the doctors
38. Residence of Dr. Bond
39. Hospital for Non-lepers
40. Residence of Pastor Manson
41. Residence built by the Memorial
42. Residence built by the Memorial
43. Residence of the Chief Chemist
44. Residences of light materials built by the Memorial for the minor personnel
45. Bachelors' Quarters
46. Administration Building
47. Ned Ferguson's (Langford) house

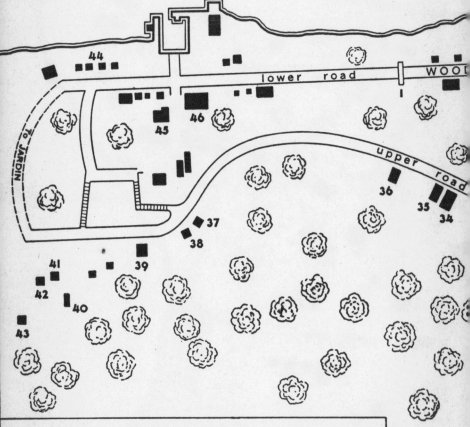

TOPOGRAPHICAL SKETCH OF CULION

An aerial view of Culion showing the colony in the center, the inner bay at the lower left, the island of Busuanga, across the upper third of the picture, and many smaller islands in the China Sea.

Culion

Culion
Island

(Palawan Prov.)

AVENUE

To PILAPILAN